LIBBY
ZNAIMER
IN CANCER
LAND

LIBBY ZNAIMER

IN CANCER LAND

LIVING WELL
IS THE BEST REVENGE

KEY PORTER  BOOKS

Library and Archives Canada Cataloguing in Publication
Znaimer, Libby

In cancerland: living well is the best revenge / Libby Znaimer.

ISBN 978-1-55263-947-4

1. Znaimer, Libby. 2. Breast--Cancer--Patients--Biography. I. Title.

RC280.B8Z563 2007   362.196'994490092   C2007-901959-5

ONTARIO ARTS COUNCIL
CONSEIL DES ARTS DE L'ONTARIO

The publisher gratefully acknowledges the support of the Canada Council for the Arts and the Ontario Arts Council for its publishing program. We acknowledge the support of the Government of Ontario through the Ontario Media Development Corporation's Ontario Book Initiative.

We acknowledge the financial support of the Government of Canada through the Book Publishing Industry Development Program (BPIDP) for our publishing activities.

Key Porter Books Limited
Six Adelaide Street East, Tenth Floor
Toronto, Ontario
Canada M5C 1H6

www.keyporter.com

Text design: Martin Gould
Electronic formatting: Jean Lightfoot Peters

Printed and bound in Canada
07 08 09 10 11   5 4 3 2 1

Contents

1   The Lump   1

2   The Diagnosis   7

3   The Options   15

4   Surgical Decisions   23

5   Cancergirl in Cancerland   35

6   Cancer and the Spouse   49

7   Chemotherapy   57

8   The Hair Thing   71

9   Cancer and Friends   103

10 The Gene People   115

11 Radiation   131

12 Cancer and Work   145

13	The Other C-Word	153
14	The Good News About Cancer	165
15	The Final Surgery	175
16	Cosmetics	181
17	Leaving Cancerland	191
18	Why I Hate the Word *Survivor*	201
	Index	207

To

My mother, Chaya, for her example

and

My husband, Doug, for his love and care

Acknowledgements

I WOULD LIKE to thank everyone who encouraged me to write this book, and who helped make it a reality. My agent, Anne McDermid, who championed this project. The team at Key Porter: including my excellent editor, Clare McKeon, art director Martin Gould, Paula Sloss, Rob Howard, and Jordan Fenn. A number of people who gave me invaluable advice and support: my brother Moses Znaimer, Richard Lumsden, Erik Morin, Eithne McCredie, Barbara Moses, Marc Glassman, George Whiteside, Thien Le, and my wonderful husband, Doug Goold, who is also my editor-for-life.

Thanks also to the *National Post*, where I first wrote about my experience with cancer, and my editor there, Sarah Murdoch.

Finally, I want to express my gratitude to those who—to quote an ancient Hebrew prayer—kept me in life, sustained me, and enabled me to reach this season: my family, friends, and caregivers. I want to reiterate how lucky I am to have these people in my life: in addition to those I have already named, they are Sam Znaimer, Marilyn Lightstone, Jodi Lofchy, Barb Pathy, Michina Pope, Elsa Reia, and Vicki Russell; as well as my doctors, Angel Arnaout, Jean-Philippe Pignol, Ellen Warner, and Joan Murphy; and nurse oncologist Anita McGowan.

1

The Lump

"That's a lump," I say aloud, in bed, in the middle of the night. "A lump," I repeat, first softly and then louder. My husband wakes up. He can feel it too. "You're right," Doug whispers. "Thank goodness you found it."

It is a long time before I fall back asleep, and I am soon awakened by a terrifying dream: I am barring the door against an intruder. I'm pushing with all my strength, but he's getting in.

IF IT HADN'T BEEN SO HOT, I might not have found the lump when I did. It was an unseasonably sweltering night, the last of May, and the heat woke me up around 2 a.m. As I pulled the sheet away from me, my hand grazed my bare breast and I felt it. I thought I must be mistaken and touched it again, then again. My breasts are dense, full of bumps and valleys. Like most women,

I've had many lectures about breast self-examination, and I've always worried I wouldn't be able to distinguish a lump from the normal landscape of my breast. But, believe me, there's no mistaking the real thing.

The discovery of the lump that night started a chain of events that overtook my life. I wrote this account of my experience and what I learned, where I turned for answers, and how I navigated the health-care system in the hope that it will help other women. I wrote about what frightened me and what reassured me. I started as a terrified, newly diagnosed patient, but I found a way to live, and live well, amid the uncertainty of a cancer diagnosis.

The morning after finding the lump, I phoned my GP and was told she didn't have a slot that day to see me. Apparently, a two-centimetre lump in the breast was not a good enough reason to add ten minutes to her day. So I phoned my brother's GP. His office called back, telling me to come in any time in the afternoon.

I saw Dr. Robert Kingstone at 3 p.m., and within minutes he confirmed what I already knew. "You're not hallucinating," he told me. "That's definitely a lump." While I sat in his office, he booked a mammogram and ultrasound for eleven the next morning.

What shocked me about the discovery of the lump was that I had had my annual mammogram and ultrasound just ten weeks before and was told that everything was fine. Now, that earlier screening gave me hope. Whatever this was hadn't been there two months ago.

If I hadn't been given the all-clear on my annual mammogram, I wouldn't have been surprised to find myself one of the twenty-two thousand Canadian women diagnosed with breast cancer every year. One in nine women develops the disease during her lifetime, and I'd always known that I might be the one, because my mother had breast cancer.

I remember my brother Sam and me being taken to stay with a neighbour while Mummy had an operation. Our brother, Moses, was old enough to remain at home. When we returned a few days later, she was in bed, and a sadness seemed to hang over everything. My father came home soon after with a beautiful shiny box. Was it a get-well gift? That would have been unusual. My parents were post-war refugees, and money was very tight. Anything extra always went on the children. I took a peek inside the box when no one was around and discovered the largest bra I'd ever seen, the left side filled with what I now know was a prosthetic breast.

My mother quickly accepted her new body and moved on with her life. Where her left breast had been, her chest was concave, with a bluish tinge. Her left underarm was completely carved out where the lymph nodes had been removed. She never hid it from us, and I came to see it as normal.

My mother—Chaya to her close-knit circle of immigrant friends, Helen to everyone else—beat the odds. Doctors say about 60 per cent of women diagnosed in the 1960s lived for five years but far fewer were around to mark the tenth anniversary of their diagnosis. Today, the five-year survival rate is 86 per cent, and most of those women are still around ten, fifteen, even twenty years later, a consequence of earlier diagnosis and better treatment. My mother lived another thirty years before dying of ovarian cancer.

Dr. Richard Margolese, one of Canada's foremost experts on breast cancer—who, coincidentally, treated my mother in her later years—is gratified by these advances. He is a professor of surgical oncology at McGill University, and he practises at the Jewish General Hospital in Montreal. "We've moved from radical disfiguring surgery with limited cure rates to breast-conserving surgery and improved cure rates," he says. "I feel terrific about that."

He believes chemotherapy is the chief reason for the improvement. Forty-four years ago, after her operation, my mother had only one option—cobalt, an early form of radiation.

Unlike many high-risk people I know, I have never brooded about breast cancer, though I knew it could happen. I think I've been realistic. The Canadian Cancer Society recommends that all women between the ages of fifty and sixty-nine have a mammogram every two years and that starting at age forty, they talk about their risk of breast cancer with their doctors to determine whether they should start screening sooner. Obviously, women with a very strong family history should start before forty. I've had annual mammograms since the age of thirty-five and recently started having ultrasounds. Originally I was in a screening program at Toronto Western Hospital, but in recent years my GP sent me to a private clinic. I'd never really considered issues of competence.

I think the most enduring effect of seeing the result of a radical mastectomy for most of my childhood is that I have always been inclined to show off my breasts. And, as it happened, I was just about to change into a décolleté outfit when the doctor called me with the results of that morning's mammogram and ultrasound. "The lump is suspicious for cancer because it has stalactites," he told me.

I knew what that meant: cancerous lumps are star-shaped; benign lumps are round. He told me the next step was to see a breast surgeon and have a biopsy and promised to get me an appointment quickly.

After I put down the phone, I went out into the garden, as if in slow motion. Everything looked the same but was entirely different. There was Doug, in his usual seat under the trellis. I told him the news, and he did his best to comfort me. We had planned on going out that night, but he assured me that we didn't have to go anywhere or do anything.

I was upset but determined to continue with our plans. Actually, I was hell-bent on having as good a time as possible. Call me shallow, but planning to attend two fabulous events just hours after hearing such bad news made me feel I was coping. So I put on my revealing dress for our night on the town.

When we arrived at one of Toronto's restaurants-of-the-moment, it was packed with partygoers. As soon as our host saw me, he bellowed by way of greeting, "A hint of tit!" Suddenly, everyone was staring at my breasts.

2

The Diagnosis

The panic rises as I stare at the phone. Why won't it ring? Dr. Kingstone's office manager, Gail, promised that getting me in with a breast surgeon was her top priority. That was more than twenty-four hours ago. Now the weekend is looming. Maybe I should try someone else. Frantic, I begin calling other doctors I know. When one finally picks up, the response is not reassuring. "Be prepared to call in every favour you've ever done," she says. "And you still may have to go to the States to get in quickly."

DR. KINGSTONE TOLD ME he suspected I had breast cancer on a Thursday afternoon. He promised he'd get me an appointment with a breast surgeon very soon. When I didn't hear back by the weekend, I decided to go to Plan B. I left a message for my gynecologist, who called me back on Monday morning to say she was referring me to the Toronto Sunnybrook Regional Cancer Centre, for which she had a high regard. She was sure I'd get a booking for that week. But I quickly learned that none was available.

By the close of business on Monday, I had two appointments, but neither was soon enough. Dr. Kingstone's office had indeed nailed down a booking, at Mount Sinai Hospital's Marvelle Koffler Breast Centre. But I would have to wait three agonizing weeks. Or I could go with my gynecologist's referral and see a doctor at Sunnybrook a few days earlier. I was beside myself. When Dr. Kingstone had examined me four days earlier, he checked the radiologist's written report on my annual mammogram, the one I'd had ten weeks earlier. There was no mention there of a suspicious, star-shaped golf ball in my bosom. Now, that mammogram made me feel anything but reassured. If it had grown to this size in ten weeks, how could it be safe to wait another three?

My gynecologist advised me to contact CAREpath, a company that runs a cancer assistance program. I wondered whether this would be my first foray into the dreaded second tier of the health system that so many Canadians, including me, are worried about. But I was a whole lot more worried about getting treatment, so I called. The office manager began to describe the services. "There's just one thing I want to know," I interrupted. "Can you make this go faster?"

A few hours later the company's CEO and majority owner, Dr. Denny DePetrillo, called. He's a gynecologic oncologist and a former chief of surgical oncology at Cancer Care Ontario, the Ontario provincial agency set up to oversee cancer treatment. "Speed is not the critical factor here," he told me. "The most important thing is to have the right team of doctors, who will make the right treatment decisions. If you're rushed onto the operating table before they have all the information, you could end up having to go back for more surgery."

Dr. DePetrillo believes that we have high-quality cancer care in Ontario, but that there are gaps in what he calls the infrastructure. And one of those gaps is funding to shepherd patients through the system. "People go through a maze of programs at different hospitals, and there's no one person who can be their key contact through the whole process," he said. "That's what we offer here." CAREpath reviews patients' results and lets them know if they're getting what they need. It also provides up to ten hours of phone counselling with a nurse oncologist to help clients navigate the system. These services are paid for through company health-insurance plans and employee-assistance programs.

My conversation with Dr. DePetrillo was reassuring, but it didn't get me any closer to an appointment—or to the decision about which of the two appointments that I already had I would keep.

So I called my friend Mel, who is a prominent doctor in another field. "Both places are excellent," he said. "Whatever you do, don't wait to be treated at one instead of the other. Take the first appointment you can get." He also told me not to worry about the surgeon. "I don't mean to belittle your situation, but it's not rocket science. The treatment of breast cancer has come a long way, and it's pretty standard. If they find X, they do Y, if they find Y, they do Z." But Mel promised to check out the surgeons anyway.

I found the idea that I had a garden-variety disease that is treatable very reassuring.

Days went by, and I still hadn't discovered a way to get a faster appointment. But if there's one thing I've learned in my years as a journalist covering CEOs, politicians, and other decision makers, it is this: if you want something done, call the assistant. Assistants control schedules and set priorities. I called the Sunnybrook surgeon's secretary, Susan, and left a voice mail that was answered within minutes. But not with the words I wanted to hear.

Susan told me the surgeon had office hours at Sunnybrook once a week, but her upcoming clinic had been cancelled, so she wouldn't even be in until the day I was scheduled to see her. Like some of the other breast cancer specialists at Sunnybrook, this surgeon also worked at Women's College Hospital. Women's College and Sunnybrook were once amalgamated, but are now once more separate. The surgeon would be seeing patients at Women's College sooner than she would at Sunnybrook, but my referral was for Sunnybrook, so I couldn't use it at Women's College.

Dumb bureaucratic rules. I was stunned. But then a couple of minutes later, Susan called back to say she'd found a way to untangle the red tape. The surgeon would see me a week ahead of schedule, at Women's College. That would make it slightly more than two weeks after I'd found the lump.

In preparation for my appointment, I picked up the films from the annual mammograms I'd had in March and the one I'd had recently.

Now I wanted to find out everything I could about the surgeon who would hold my life in her hands. But before I had completed my Google research, Mel called to say he'd heard she was excellent. That was good enough for me. In the days leading up to my appointment, I started dreaming of her. In my imagination, she was a frumpy woman in her late fifties and very stern.

In fact, Dr. Angel Arnaout was the exact opposite of the surgeon I had conjured up in my dreams. A warm and elegant woman, she is physically striking—tall, slim, extremely well put together, immaculate in fact. The day I met her she was wearing a white pinstriped pantsuit with coordinated accessories, including a Muslim headscarf that matched her belt. The fashion quotient made me identify with her immediately. I actually found it reassuring, because I knew she'd understand that it was important to me to look good in my clothes when the surgery was over. I remember how hard it was for my mother, after her radical mastectomy more than forty years ago, to find things that fit properly. I cringe when I recall seeing her in outfits that made her prosthesis obvious.

The hijab wasn't the only thing about her appearance that surprised me. Once I was inside her office, I found myself staring at her, trying to detect a crow's foot, a laugh line, the hint of a wrinkle. My God, I wondered, is she even thirty?

Surgeons, as we know from television, don't always have good bedside manners. But Dr. Arnaout's was terrific. The first thing she asked was whether I had family. I told her my husband was in the waiting room. She got up from behind the desk, went out, and invited Doug to join us.

When I was on the examination table, she was comforting and reassuring but without sugar-coating reality. "Yes, we have to investigate the lump," she said, "but your breasts and underarms do not show any other visible signs of cancer, and that's very good news."

I found only one benefit to having a lump the size of an apricot: the doctor could perform a needle biopsy right on the spot. Otherwise, I would have had to wait another two weeks to have it done by a radiologist. Dr. Arnaout called in her nurse clinician, Claudia, and suggested Doug leave the room. "Actually, you can stay if you want," she said, "but some husbands have been known to faint." "Doug doesn't have to be here," I laughed.

The biopsy involved extracting tissue samples with a large needle that sounded like a staple gun coming down on my chest. It was painful and distressing. Dr. Arnaout kept apologizing, telling me if the sample wasn't big enough, the test could come back inconclusive, and everything would have to be done again. When she finished, she waved the vial in front of me, as if I could tell the difference. The samples would go to a laboratory, and it would be a week before I got the results. Sometimes it takes even longer.

Dr. Arnaout kept telling me not to worry. When the procedure was over, I was ready to take her advice. I asked whether I'd need surgery if the lump was benign. "That's up to you," she said. "It depends what you want." But she didn't leave it at that.

"The chances that this is not cancer," she told me frankly, "are very slim."

3

The Options

I should have cancelled this meeting. I'm waiting for an important phone call from Dr. Arnaout's office. But I'm trying to live my life as normally as possible, and I figure that talking business with a colleague will at least take my mind off things. The phone rings. I excuse myself and walk onto the patio, which is mercifully empty. But I'm not prepared for what Claudia, Dr. Arnaout's nurse clinician, tells me.

"Our radiologists have gone over all your films, and the problem area is bigger than we first thought. They're not sure if you have one big lump or three smaller ones," she says.

I can barely breathe. I try to process what she has just said. They examined "all" my films. "Are you telling me the lump or lumps were on the annual mammograms that were done at the private clinic ten weeks ago, and they were missed?"

"Yes," she says. "It means we're not sure if we can offer you a lumpectomy or if you'll have to have a mastectomy."

I fight off the tears. I feel like a bomb has just exploded on me. I am shattered. I also feel a little ridiculous. Here I am on the patio of the gorgeous, hip, private Spoke Club. What in the world am I doing here? My fabulous life is falling apart.

A mastectomy—my mother's surgery—was the one scenario I dreaded. I wasn't prepared to face it. My diagnosis hadn't even been officially confirmed yet.

AFTER PERFORMING THE needle biopsy, Dr. Arnaout had told me she was almost certain I had breast cancer. I was glad she did. She had been mostly so upbeat during our meeting that I could have spent the next week clinging to the hope that the lump was nothing. Instead, during the week-long wait for the results from the laboratory, I had time to get used to the idea that I had cancer. But this was not the cancer I had in mind.

At each stage, I found it easiest to process bad news in small bits. It would have been impossible to make a mental leap from *healthy person* to *cancer patient* overnight. Instead, I moved gradually from gnawing uncertainty to the grim realization that I had cancer.

After talking to Dr. Arnaout, I made a point of seeing how long I could go without thinking or talking about the C-word. I found that as long as I was immersed in a distracting activity such as Sudoku or a lecture, interview, or performance, I could keep my mind off it.

The opening of Toronto's new opera house the evening after I visited Dr. Arnaout was the perfect distraction. I had anticipated, correctly, that the biopsy would leave a bruise, which meant the strapless number I'd chosen for the occasion would no longer be an option. Doug rushed a suit to the cleaners for me. But I needed to buy some shoes. *How can a person with cancer waste over an hour searching for the perfect shoes?* I wondered. But that's exactly what I did.

At least the strappy gold sandals were on sale!

So I had accepted the idea of a manageable, early stage cancer when I got a phone call from the imaging department at Women's College Hospital the following Monday. They wanted me to come in for further mammograms and an ultrasound. Dr. Arnaout hadn't mentioned further mammograms and ultrasounds.

The need for more tests set off alarm bells, so I phoned her nurse clinician, Claudia, to ask what was going on. Her return call was the one I took at the Spoke Club. I was surprised that she answered me so honestly. This was the most upsetting phone call of my life, and it was my fault that I had chosen to hear this news in a public place.

I have no recollection of what I said to my colleague when I returned from the patio or how I ended the meeting. I called my friend Eithne, who works a few blocks from the Spoke Club, and she offered cappuccino and comfort. Eithne has gone through breast cancer with a number of her friends, and her father, the late Dr. John

McCredie, was an eminent breast surgeon in London, Ontario. I left her office feeling that I could cope.

But as soon as Doug got home, I started crying uncontrollably. "My beautiful breasts," I wailed. "It's going to be fine," he told me, "and I don't care what it looks like." No one could have asked for a more supportive spouse. He just held me, and that was exactly what I needed. Finally, I pulled myself together. I was still upset, but now I was also angry.

My thoughts returned to those first mammograms back on March 15. The clinic had called back the following day, a Thursday, asking me to come back for another series of mammograms. The receptionist took great care to reassure me. "All it means is that the radiologist saw something he didn't like or can't explain," she said. "We call back 20 per cent to 25 per cent of our patients, and it almost always turns out to be nothing."

I wasn't overly worried. I had been called back for more pictures once before, and it had, in fact, turned out to be nothing. So I returned the next afternoon. Traffic was terrible and I was late. When I'd had the mammogram, the technician told me the radiologist had already left for the day. She told me to wait, then she left the room.

After what seemed like an eternity, she came back with a big smile. "I ran after him in the parking lot, and he came back to look at your mammogram," she said. "I didn't want you to worry needlessly all weekend. He says everything is just fine."

"That was kind," I said, thanking her. But, still, I was uncomfortable that my mammogram was read by someone who was rushing off for the weekend, probably after a very hard week. The technician assured me that the report wouldn't be written up until Monday, and she was right. But did the radiologist take a second look at the mammogram, or did he write the report from his notes? I have no way of knowing. What I do know is that he wrote: "The suspected area of architectural distortion is entirely normal."

I had also had an ultrasound, and there had been something worrying on my ultrasound too—not an obvious malignancy but, in medical lingo, "an area of hyperechoic tissue." In his report, however, the radiologist dismissed this as being "of no clinical significance."

Just ten weeks later, after I showed him the lump, Dr. Kingstone had sent me to the same private clinic for another mammogram. This time another radiologist read the films and came to an entirely different conclusion—that I required a surgical consultation and a biopsy. How could this happen? This was not a matter of the first radiologist missing something microscopic. My tumour was large.

After years of public education, women believe that regular mammograms provide the best hope of early detection. Every year, two million mammograms are done in Canada, at a cost of about $200 million in public funds. Mammograms—at least the analogue mammograms I had—are an imperfect technology, especially for younger women. They are only 50 per cent to 55 per cent accurate for women under fifty or women who have dense breasts. But how many of us have stopped to consider the quality of the machines and the skill of the radiologists?

"A bad mammogram is worse than no mammogram at all," said Normand Laberge, CEO of the Canadian Association of Radiologists. He was referring to the quality of the films, not the way they are read. Clinics must meet rigorous standards in order to be accredited by his association, he said. One of the requirements is that mammogram films must be free of what the experts call "technical artifacts"—for example, dust, dirt, or any spot that could interfere with an accurate reading. Too many artifacts and a clinic will lose its certification. In his report on my mammogram, the radiologist interpreted the suspicious area in my breast as a technical artifact.

I went for my fourth mammogram and ultrasound of the year on June 22. The doctors at the Henrietta Banting Breast Centre at Women's College Hospital decided I would also need an MRI before they could decide on a course of treatment, a prospect I dreaded because I'm a bit claustrophobic. The next day, I went to Sunnybrook for the breast MRI, which took forty-five minutes, during which I had to remain still within the imaging tube, my head barely poking out. I got through it with the help of Ativan (generic name: lorazepam), which is a tranquilizer, and a lovely nurse named Stacey.

I was attending the three-day ideaCity Conference that day. The conference is produced by my brother Moses Znaimer, and it's an eclectic gathering of artists, authors, cosmologists, and doctors, among others. Every year there are a number of different themes, and because of the timing of my MRI appointment, I missed most of the morning that was devoted to one of my favourite topics: sex. I arrived at the theatre just in time to catch the last presentation, a video of a couple making love in an MRI machine!

4

Surgical Decisions

No matter how many scientific explanations I hear, I feel there has to be a "moment" when the cancer spreads, and there is no doctor on Earth who can guarantee my "moment" won't occur while I am waiting for my operation.

AT MY SECOND appointment with Dr. Arnaout, she gave me the results of the biopsy; they confirmed her suspicion of breast cancer. Because of my earlier phone call with her nurse clinician, Claudia, I was already grappling with the possibility that I wouldn't be eligible for breast-conserving surgery. So I barely reacted when Dr. Arnaout uttered the words "invasive ductile carcinoma."

Dr. Arnaout told me she had to confirm whether the three lumps the Women's College radiologist had noted were in the same quadrant of my breast. "Imagine it's a pudding with different things inside it," explained Dr. Arnaout. "We think the lumps are like raisins in the same pudding, and if that's the case, we'll be able to do a lumpectomy."

I found it very reassuring that Dr. Arnaout wasn't making this decision on her own. Like many other hospitals, Women's College holds regular multidisciplinary cancer conferences, where doctors from a broad range of specialties—surgeons, oncologists, radiologists, and pathologists—get together to review individual cases and decide on the best treatment. The conference on my case was to be held on the last Tuesday in June. In the meantime, I had more mammograms, ultrasounds, and the MRI. I was on track for surgery in the first week of July—not a moment too soon from my point of view.

I thought I was prepared for anything when, once again, a phone call caught me up—a simple voice mail from the Imaging Department at Women's College. I had an appointment for an ultrasound on my right breast. My *right* breast? Did the MRI find cancer there too? I was practically beside myself.

Dr. Arnaout had given me her pager number. I considered this a privilege, and I did not want to abuse it. But I decided to call even though I was to see her again the next morning. "We saw a lump in your right breast, but it is definitely benign," she assured me. "We just want to map it." Never have I been so relieved. Imagine feeling fortunate to have cancer in just one breast!

Doug and I arrived at Dr. Arnaout's office the next morning primed to hear the decision on my surgery. But there was no resolution that day. "I'd like to postpone your surgery by a week," Dr. Arnaout told us. In most cases, she explained, the MRI shows things that cannot be seen on a mammogram. In other words, cases usually look more serious on the MRI.

In my case, the opposite was true. The most recent mammogram, the one done at the hospital the week before, looked worse than the one I'd had done at the beginning of June. But the MRI showed less disease. The doctors from the multidisciplinary conference also thought the latest mammograms were showing a hematoma, meaning an internal bruise, from the biopsy. They wanted a few more pictures so they could decide exactly how big my tumour was and whether those three lumps could be treated as one mass.

This was a far cry from the "garden variety" cancer I thought I had when I first found the lump, all those weeks ago. The diagnosis may have been straightforward; the treatment plan was anything but. And it was by sheer luck that I found the perfect person to turn to, right down the street, at a neighbour's house.

My friend and former neighbour Anne-Marie was visiting. We hadn't been in touch since a round of goodbye parties for her and her family about three years before. Anne-Marie is a radiologist specializing in breasts, one of the best in North America. She left Toronto for one of the famed Mayo clinics in Wisconsin. She now heads the radiology department there.

Anne-Marie knew some of the doctors on my team and told me she had no doubt they'd come up with the best treatment plan. Then came the zinger. "Mastectomy with immediate reconstruction may be the best thing for you," she said. We soon moved from a glass of wine on the porch to a boozy dinner, during which Anne-Marie pronounced, "Everything I know about you suggests one thing: you have bad genes!"

In the mid-1990s, scientists mapping the human genome discovered three mutations in BRCA-1 and BRCA-2, the genes that normally protect women from breast and ovarian cancer. These genetic alterations account for only about 5 per cent of breast cancer cases, but they are much more common in the Ashkenazi Jewish population. While the risk for the general population is 13 per cent, women with these mutations have a 50 per cent to 80 per cent risk of developing breast cancer. The fact that my mother had both breast and ovarian cancer was a red flag to doctors, who figured she probably had the gene, and so did I. Eventually, the genetic testing proved them right.

Dr. Arnaout had said she was going to refer me for genetic testing. I hadn't given it much thought. At this point, genetic testing seemed a bit like closing the barn door after the horses escaped. But if I had one of the breast cancer mutations, it would put me at risk for more breast and ovarian cancers. It would mean this could happen again. "If you have the gene, maybe you should bite the bullet," said Anne-Marie, "and get both your breasts removed, as well as your ovaries and tubes."

Now I was really scared. My benchmark has always been my mother's experience. She had breast cancer and she survived for another thirty years. That's why I never even entertained the possibility that I could die of this. Ovarian cancer is another story. That's what killed my mother, and it was a horrible death.

I was soon focusing on the possibility of getting ovarian cancer instead of concentrating on the breast cancer I already had. Anne-Marie pulled me back to reality. "You have to deal with the disease you have before anything else," she said. "The rest can come later."

I was trying to move forward when one of my tests pulled me back into the past. I was having an ultrasound and it was very uncomfortable. The technician, a very sympathetic woman named Thelma, kept apologizing. "It's really important for me to press hard," she said. "Otherwise, I won't see the edges of the tumour." I was beside myself, but not because of anything Thelma was doing. It seemed like a completely different test than any breast ultrasound I'd had before. By comparison, the ultrasounds I'd had at the private clinic felt like a once-over lightly. Could that be the reason they failed to detect an obvious malignancy?

The ultrasound seemed to take forever. Thelma left the room to check the films and returned a minute later with the radiologist, Dr. Belinda Curpen, who is considered an expert in mammography. "You're a friend of

Anne-Marie's," she said brightly, "I'm sorry about your diagnosis." She told me she'd had some questions about my case from the doctors who were reviewing it. "Since I was here today anyway, I thought I'd stop by." With that, she picked up the ultrasound wand and began doing the test herself.

I practically burst into tears. I had been struggling for weeks to make sure I had the best care possible, and the stress was getting to me. Now I was overwhelmed with gratitude for the care and concern I was receiving.

Dr. Curpen had no trouble deciding what she was seeing on the ultrasound screen. She told me that in her opinion, the three lumps were part of a single mass. That's why I wasn't surprised, a few days later, when Dr. Arnaout told me she had good news. "At the conference on your case, we decided to recommend a lumpectomy," she said. "By the way, the decision was unanimous."

That meant I would have my surgery on July 11, six weeks after finding the lump, and three weeks after my diagnosis was confirmed. Even though a series of doctors had explained that speed was not a critical factor, I couldn't wait to get the cancer out of me. Dr. Arnaout told me about a study that found no difference in outcome as long as patients had surgery within three months of diagnosis. But that didn't make me any less anxious to excise the cancer.

I had become obsessed with finding out when and why cancer spreads! The answer is complicated. It's not just a function of size, as I originally thought. Chemical changes

in the tumour allow it to spread, and every tumour is different. Some cancers spread when they are tiny; some
remain contained even though they are large. But I was
convinced there had to be a "moment" when the cancer
spreads. And I didn't want my moment to occur while I
was waiting for my operation.

I will know if the cancer has spread to my lymph nodes as soon as I
wake up from surgery. If I feel a drain under my left arm, the
answer will be yes. If not, I will be home free.

IN MY MOTHER'S DAY, the surgeons would
remove all the underarm lymph nodes that drained from
the breast. She ended up with terrible, debilitating
swelling of her left arm—lymphedema. I love playing tennis, and I was as worried about my game as anything else.

Now there is a new technique, sentinel node biopsy.
The day before surgery, doctors inject dye into the breast
to find the lymph node or nodes where the breast drains
first before moving on to the other nodes. That's the sentinel node, and if the cancer hasn't spread there, it hasn't
gone anywhere else either. (I had one sentinel node, most
people have two, but you can have up to five.) The surgeon
removes the sentinel node, and a pathologist looks at it
under a microscope while you're on the operating table. If
your sentinel node is clear, they close you up, and there's
no need for a drain. If not, they remove the rest of your
lymph nodes.

When I went up to Sunnybrook Hospital for my sentinel node injection, I was delighted to find Dr. Lisa Ehrlich, a specialist in nuclear medicine. She remembered me from the mid-1990s when she had treated me for a thyroid problem. "Don't worry," she comforted me. "Breast cancer isn't what it used to be. These days, eh, you live with it." I certainly hoped so.

"We think we got it all." All the anxiety I'd been feeling lifts as soon as I hear these words from Dr. Arnaout. I am waking up from the surgery—without a drain—and I feel that I have my life back. Yes, I still face months of treatment—involving chemotherapy, radiation, hair loss, nausea, and then more surgery. In my initial euphoria, all of this is an unpleasant but necessary clean-up operation. In my mind, the cancer journey is starting to be over.

DR. ARNAOUT HAD warned me before the surgery that we would have to wait for the final pathology before we could be sure of the results.

For many patients, the two-week wait for the report from the lab is unbearable. Although they've heard the preliminary results from the operating room, the uncertainty that remains makes this period one of the most difficult in the entire process. I had a very different attitude. I knew I would have to wait for a month after surgery before I could start chemotherapy. Because there was nothing I could do, I was happy to bask in the good news, even if it might turn out to be illusory. A two-week vacation from cancer would be better than nothing.

Dr. Arnaout had already told me that based on the size of my tumour, she was going to recommend chemotherapy, whether the cancer had spread or not. I cut her off when she started to explain why this was necessary. I understood that the chemotherapy was insurance, and I was happy to take it.

I wasn't thinking about any of this when I opened my eyes in the recovery room, however. I wasn't even groggy. I woke up feeling alert, hungry, and craving caffeine. After a couple of hours, I could walk to the bathroom by myself. I even mustered the courage to look at my left breast. All taped up, it didn't look half bad. I was ready to go home.

Once I got home, I didn't feel like going to bed. I helped Doug cook dinner, and we lingered over it in our beautiful garden. I didn't take the painkillers we'd picked up on the way home. Later, I settled into bed with pillows elevating my arm. My rate of recovery seemed unbelievable.

You know what they say about things that seem too good to be true....

A few hours later I was awakened—by a strange sloshing noise inside my body. Doug wasn't there beside me. It was very hot, and since I was doing so well, he'd gone to sleep in a cooler room. I felt a lot weaker when I walked to the bathroom this time. My left breast had swollen to elephantine proportions. Suddenly, I didn't have the strength to open the bottle of painkillers. One squeeze of the container and everything went black.

Doug was there in a flash. "Don't get up," he yelled. "Let's at least get you away from the marble floor and onto the carpet." For some reason, it seemed critical to me that I get back on my feet as soon as possible. I insisted on trying to stand, and down I went again.

"I didn't ask for a double-D cup," I joked with Dr. Arnaout the next morning. She told me the swelling was called a seroma, and it was completely normal. Nature abhors a vacuum, and fluid had moved in to replace the tissue she had taken out during the operation. The bigger the hole, the more fluid that moves in. She had removed between four and five centimetres, that's why the swelling was so big.

The bruise that had started to spread was more troubling. This is also a normal side effect. I have a tendency to bruise easily and wasn't too concerned. Dr. Arnaout said it was a hematoma, an internal bruise with dried blood. There was no way of knowing whether it was a result of the surgery or of my fall in the bathroom. Dr. Arnaout told me the best thing would be if my body reabsorbed all these fluids on its own. If not, she might have to remove them with a needle. And if the area became infected, I'd need drugs. She was going to be away for a few days, so she wrote a prescription for antibiotics. "Don't take them unless it becomes inflamed or you get a fever," she cautioned.

In the days after my operation, I became the best customer at the Women's College Henrietta Banting Breast

Centre. Claudia, Dr. Arnaout's nurse clinician, had infinite patience for my phone calls and visits. For a patient, it can be hard to tell whether a bruised and swollen area is getting worse. Twice, I had a little bleeding. It turned out that I had inadvertently pulled off some some adhesive skin closures, the bandages surgeons use instead of sutures. It was nothing, but I had no way of knowing that.

After about a week, the breast started to get smaller, and I could wear T-shirts without looking too lopsided. Every day, I felt a bit stronger, and I was almost back to my normal routine. I had been told it could take weeks or even months for the swelling to settle.

Two weeks after the operation, I had my final appointment with Dr. Arnaout. I'd been so wrapped up in the side effects of the surgery that I'd barely wondered about that crucial pathology report. The news was very good. They did, in fact, get everything. The tumour turned out to be 2.5 centimetres and Stage 2 breast cancer—some cause for euphoria. I made an appointment for a six-month follow-up and hugged Dr. Arnaout goodbye.

Just one day later, I could have sworn the swelling was getting worse. I was feeling more tired, but I chalked that up to the heat and a houseful of visitors. I wasn't about to call the hospital again. I should have. I woke up in the early hours of Sunday morning bleeding through the incision.

The first stop was the emergency room at Women's College. It is a bare bones operation, with only one nurse and doctor overnight. After a quick look and a phone call, the doctor sent us uptown to Sunnybrook Hospital. I needed another operation. I was angry and upset, and wondering whether I had brought this on myself. I opted to wait twenty-four hours so Dr. Arnaout, who was out of town, could perform the procedure. "Did you play tennis?" That was the first thing Dr. Arnaout asked when she saw the open wound in my chest. Thankfully, I hadn't.

The second surgery took only ten minutes. Dr. Arnaout removed a hematoma the size of a plum. This time, it was harder to recover from the anaesthetic, and this time the doctor was strict. No exercise! I wasn't even allowed to drive until the healing was well underway.

In fact, the complications were as much in my head as in my body. What I had in mind was a fast, firm recovery. I had decided what kind of cancer patient I was going to be—a tennis-playing, gym-going alpha female who doesn't miss a beat! Now I had to struggle to put this into perspective. *Okay, it was just a minor setback. I celebrated too soon, that's all.*

"I'm so happy," Dr. Arnaout exclaimed a few days later when she examined me. She had insisted on seeing me before she left for her summer holiday. Now, I figured, it was safe to celebrate.

But with chemotherapy set to begin in just a few weeks, it was going to have to be a very fast party.

5

Cancergirl in Cancerland

How can someone with cancer go shoe shopping? How can someone with cancer go to lunch? Or make small talk? I ask myself these questions as I try to get on with my day. I forget about my condition as soon as I get busy. So I have to keep reminding myself. And every time, I wonder whether a shift in priorities is in order. That's probably a good thing.

But who is this someone with cancer? I'm suddenly thinking of myself in the third person. It's as though the word me and the word cancer can't inhabit the same thought.

AS THE DAYS PASSED, I got closer to this someone with cancer. I gave her a name: Cancergirl. It sounds light and frivolous as I read it on the page, but inside my head, in those first few weeks, it had a contemptuous ring. Cancergirl is going to the store, I thought as I left the house, or Cancergirl is going to a lecture. I scolded myself: Why am I thinking of myself in such a hateful way? I didn't think cancer was shameful, but I did think of myself as someone healthy, not someone with cancer. And the worst disconnect was when I'd remember I had cancer in the middle of an ordinary activity on an ordinary day.

Cancergirl stayed with me, but I developed a better attitude toward her. I dropped the mocking tone. And I decided it was fine for Cancergirl to live my normal life. At least part of the time. Actually, I only thought of myself as Cancergirl when I was going about my regular activities. Maybe because my cancer was still a secret at that point.

On the other hand, I felt fully present when I was dealing with the cancer. It was definitely Libby who was frantically phoning doctors, trying to get appointments, and turning to old friends for advice. But it seemed as if these things were happening in a different dimension—a place that had been outside my life but was now taking it over. I called it Cancerland. It was a kind of parallel universe.

Cancerland was incredibly intense, a quiet place where everything was life and death. Nothing was trivial. It was populated with ministering angels—doctors, nurses, and administrative people who spent their days attuned to other people's tragedy. When I entered Cancerland as a patient, my first job was to take in a huge amount of information. The complicated scientific and technical knowledge was well outside my area of expertise, hard enough to understand in the abstract, that much harder when I knew it was about me. I would come home from my trips to Cancerland exhausted by the sheer volume of information. Sometimes I had the sense of being whipped with it. There was too much, and I couldn't shield myself from it or take it in without pain.

Cancerland was an indoor world. Everything happened in waiting rooms, offices, and examining rooms. Even when I met with friends, when the secret was finally out, we stayed inside to discuss the C-word.

The rest of my life was unfolding outside. It was the height of a gorgeous summer. Our beautiful backyard seemed as far as anyone could get from the ugly, sterile environment of Cancerland. I would sit in the garden and tell Doug what I had learned while he was at work. "The saving grace of all this is that it's fascinating," I would tell him. I wasn't alone in imagining Cancerland. I felt a wave of recognition a few months later when I read a story titled "Young and Breastless" in *Flare* magazine, in which a young mother named Vanessa Turke talked about her own trip to "cancer-land."

Cancerland was, ultimately, a comforting place to be. I'd had such a hard time getting into the system in those first few weeks after finding the lump that I was relieved to be on the inside. In Cancerland, cancer was normal, and I knew I'd be well taken care of.

I felt as if I was up against the deadline of my life, and I operated exactly as if I was on a breaking story. I worked the phones, trying to get in to see key people as soon as possible. I was constantly amazed to find who was happy to make time for me—and who wasn't.

Despite my family history, my GP had been unwilling to work ten extra minutes to see me the day after I found the lump—in sharp contrast to my previous family doctor, the late Dr. David Phillips. I remember calling his office several years before when I thought I felt something unusual in my breast. "Don't walk here," his secretary told me then. "Run."

I know now that delays of days, weeks, and even months don't usually make a difference. But the anxiety of walking around with a lump is unbearable. It's takes minutes for a professional to check, and that's what family doctors should do, immediately.

My sense of urgency was partly fuelled by wrong information. Ten weeks before I found the lump, my mammograms had been found normal, so I was worried I had a horribly aggressive cancer that had grown to the size of an apricot in a matter of weeks.

Those original mammograms became something of an obsession. The radiologist's mistake kept gnawing at me, more almost than the fact that I had cancer. I spent—probably wasted—a lot of my face-time with the experts trying to figure out how my cancer had been missed. Was it sheer incompetence? Or was there something about my tumour that made it hard to see on a mammogram? I eventually got some answers. The committee of doctors that reviewed my case before surgery came to the conclusion that my tumour had been plain to see on those original films. But there was no explanation about why it was missed.

———————————

"You have to get off that," says Dr. Arnaout. It's the harshest thing she's ever said to me, but of course she is right. The misread mammogram is a mistake that is over and done with, and my preoccupation with it is a tangent. I should be concentrating on healing the disease I have now. But I can't let it go.

THOSE MAMMOGRAMS weren't the only thing I wasted energy on in those early days. I was also looking for a way to get everything done faster, trying to get a fix on what my breasts would look like after surgery, and worrying that I should be getting my ovaries out at the same time. I was close to spinning out of control. The information was coming at me in a barrage, and I latched onto the latest details from whomever I happened to speak to last. Everything I learned involved a startling revelation. I desperately tried to process every bit as it came in. I found it hard, that much harder because I usually soak up facts effortlessly. Doug was with me for all my medical appointments—and not just for moral support. I knew I was incapable of taking proper notes, so he was my eyes and ears. I felt incompetent.

I was a stranger in Cancerland, and with everything so new and so traumatic, I had no sense of what was important and what wasn't, no inkling of what had to be done first. My only thought was: I want this out of me as soon as possible. Aside from my doctors, there were some key people—friends, former cancer patients, and doctors who were not treating me but did talk to me—who helped me through the process. They showed me the importance of setting priorities. They reviewed the medical stuff I didn't quite get the first time, helped me frame the right questions, and in some cases referred me to the best doctors. It's the kind of help every cancer patient needs.

"What you need is a plan," said Dr. Marla Shapiro after I inundated her with my story over the phone. My friend Dr. Trevor Born, who is a plastic surgeon, had suggested I call her. Marla had just been through her own bout with breast cancer.

A few days after we started exchanging emails, I was in Marla's den, pouring out my heart. I had gone from finding the lump, and coming to terms with the news that it was cancerous, to the horrible realization that I might need to have both my breasts and ovaries removed. It was too much to take in. Marla was practical and reassuring. "Deal with the burden of disease you have now," she told me. "Then you can decide what do about the rest." I told her about my rushed genetic tests, and how I was trying to anticipate what I would do if I had one of the breast cancer genes. "I'm trying to find a surgeon who would do an immediate breast reconstruction, if that's what I decide," I told her. She didn't mince words: "You can't keep a plastic surgeon and operating room time on hold while you make up your mind. It ain't gonna happen."

I left her house with a clear sense of my priority. It was the star-shaped, malignant lump in my left breast. Everything else could wait. Marla was one of the people who helped put me on track. She was part of the informal network that was as important as my medical team. Actually that informal network helped me find my medical team. In retrospect, I am shocked at how haphazard this process was. Newly diagnosed cancer patients need guidance. Some are lucky enough to get it from their family doctors. I didn't. There are great support groups, but I couldn't have imagined joining when I was so overwhelmed. This is the gap in our system.

That's the gap that CAREpath is trying to fill. Early on, I was consumed with getting onto the operating table as fast as possible because of my conviction that there had to be a "moment" when the cancer would spread. At that point, I thought all the extra tests my doctors wanted were just delaying my surgery and giving the cancer a chance to spread. CAREpath's Dr. DePetrillo talked me out of that. If the cancer hadn't spread now, it wouldn't in a matter of weeks or even months. Doctors had studies to prove this. It's odd, the way I perceived things back then.

Dr. DePetrillo explained that it was crucial to have all the information, that if the surgeon went in too soon, she could end up having to go in again. That chastened me. When I met with him, I was also comfortable telling him I worried about the way my breasts would look afterwards. My surgeon had explained that I'd end up with a scar and a dent. "What does she mean by a dent?" I asked him, "I can't quite imagine a fender-bender on my chest." He explained it was an indented line, almost like a wrinkle, where tissue had been removed. "It's not such a big deal," he tried to reassure me.

CAREpath clients get phone counselling from nurse oncologists, who answer all their questions and guide them through as they move from doctor to doctor, and treatment to treatment. These counsellors provide continuity and a sounding board—almost like a standing second opinion. Having this help saves patients a huge amount of stress and grief. I started working with a nurse oncologist at CAREpath, Anita, just as I was about to undergo chemotherapy. She helped me through all the tough decisions about chemotherapy and further surgery. My choices were better informed, and I felt better about making them because I was able to consult with her.

Choices are the currency of Cancerland. That opening barrage of information is just the set-up, the first part of the trip. You have to use what you learn to make decisions, and you have to do it quickly. In Cancerland, all the choices are tough.

———————————

"It's not just a matter of what the doctors tell you," says Dr. Curpen as she moves the ultrasound wand over my breast. She is the mammography expert called in to give her opinion on whether I should have a lumpectomy or a mastectomy. She is both warm and respectful. "It also depends what you want."

I say nothing, but here's what I am thinking: What I want is to live to be old!

MORE THAN FORTY years ago, when my mother had cancer, the doctors told her what to do, and she did it. Now patients are supposed take control of their health care, to be proactive, to participate, and to make informed decisions. It's better than the old days of paternalistic physicians, but it is also a burden. I read and learned a lot in the month after I found the lump. But the one thing I knew for sure was: I did not know enough to make life-and-death decisions.

I admire other women who approach these choices with a strong sense of what is right for them. I hesitated and second-guessed my instincts—partly because I'm a journalist. It's my job to gather and process large volumes of complex information on deadline. I can deliver news with authority after a brief look at the material. I am accurate but also aware of how much I don't know. When it came to my disease, I realized how superficial my understanding of cancer was.

When I'm working, I have tricks that I use to get lively, informative answers. Professional people often get caught up in jargon that no one outside their sphere understands, and they are sometimes wary about saying what they really think. I ran into the same roadblocks as a patient. Nowadays, when there are tough choices, it can be difficult to coax opinions out of your doctors. They are more comfortable presenting the options and letting the patient decide.

So I took to asking, "What would you do?" But this was only moderately useful. When my radiologist friend Anne-Marie told me to "bite the bullet" and have both my breasts and ovaries removed, all at once, as soon as possible, she was telling me what she would do. Almost all my breast cancer doctors were women, and they *all* told me they'd choose the most radical option for themselves. I think it's because they see all the worst cases. And I think it's because they are über–Type A personalities— they like to take control rather than wait and see what happens. Being a patient reinforced for me what I knew as a professional, that doctors can be notoriously tough to interview and it can be difficult to interpret their answers.

My medical oncologist at Sunnybrook Health Sciences Centre, Dr. Ellen Warner, says that overall, the new world of choice is a good thing, that patients are making better-informed choices based on a solid understanding of the risks and benefits. "For some patients, it's great. It makes them feel they have power," she said. "Others hate having the responsibility dumped on them and dealing with family members pushing and pulling."

Dr. Warner is an eminent practitioner, with a great reputation, both professional and personal. I saw her because she does a lot of work with patients like me, carriers of the breast cancer gene mutations. I think I was fated to be her patient. Before my surgery, my genetic counsellors told me they would refer me to her when the time came. Long before that happened, Dr. Warner sent me a lovely, thoughtful email after my first breast cancer column appeared in the *National Post*—at that point she had no idea she would be taking care of me.

About a quarter of cancer patients, according to Dr. Warner, want to make decisions entirely on their own. Most want to share the responsibility with their doctors. And some want to leave everything up to the physicians. "It's a bit like making financial decisions with no specialized knowledge of the markets," she said.

Some patients have a clear bottom line. "There are women who don't want to lose their *hair* no matter what, and there are women who don't want to lose their *breasts* no matter what," said Dr. Warner. Of course, some patients have more choices than others. There are fewer options for those with advanced cancer—except maybe a decision about taking part in a clinical trial. But in those cases, doctors are often clearer about what it will take to save a life.

For those with earlier stage disease there is often a vast array of choices—what kind of surgery, whether to undergo chemotherapy, what drugs to take afterwards. Dr. Warner recalls one woman who hated having to deal with it. "I was hoping you would tell me to get chemo," this patient told her. "Telling me I have an option, that's made it much harder." Dr. Warner believes that doctors have to step in for patients who are having trouble making decisions.

Sometimes patients make bad choices. Dr. Warner recalls a woman with a "horrible Stage 3 cancer," who refused chemotherapy that would have made her hair fall out. "The cancer came back a year later," she said, "and the tumour was enormous." Another woman refused treatment for ten or fifteen years "until it was a disgusting, fungating thing."

One reader of my newspaper column, a woman named Robyn, wrote me that she decided to forego chemotherapy because her cancer had not spread, even though it was Stage 3. The doctors recommended she go on tamoxifen—a chemotherapy drug many women take for five years in order to prevent a recurrence. "I have always wanted to involve homeopathic remedies, but I had a lot of resistance from the cancer experts here [at the British Columbia Cancer Agency]," wrote Robyn. "I chose not to go the drug therapy route and to concentrate on natural products and therapies to prevent recurrence."

Another woman, named Stephanie, also decided not to go on tamoxifen, because of what she called "sexual" side effects—vaginal discharge, dryness, fertility issues, hair and nail thinning, and weight gain. Thousands of women take this drug without having any of these things happen. I assume that her doctor presented drug therapy as another choice on the extensive cancer menu, that the doctor described the risks and possible side effects with no spin. Stephanie heard what she heard and decided, as a single woman, that taking this drug would ruin her sex life. Would Stephanie have made a better choice if her doctors had insisted or at least tried to convince her?

A friend of mine, Anna, decided she did not want a mastectomy even though that's what her doctors recommended. She had multi-focal disease: cancer in three separate areas of her breast. Anna insisted on having three lumpectomies instead, and the surgery was followed by more than thirty radiation treatments—many more than usual. When she told me about this, she made it clear that her decision wasn't up for discussion. Otherwise, I would have tried talking to her.

I'm sure her doctors pressed their case, but I don't know if they used the right arguments. Anna is concerned about the way she looks. I don't know if anyone explained that a reconstructed breast would probably look better than what remains after three lumpectomies. I don't know if it would have made a difference.

Anna is fine now, and I hope she stays that way. But to me, her case shows that we've moved too far from all-knowing, all-powerful doctors and passive patients. I think that when a group of good doctors agrees on what to do, a smart patient should do it.

Maybe that's why I thought of myself as Cancer*girl*, although I am very much an adult. I entered Cancerland as an ignorant girl. All I knew was that I didn't know enough to make my own decisions. I needed care, kindness, and knowledge from others. I was like a girl, needier than I had been in years, more dependent on my husband, my family, my friends, and my doctors. That's why I ultimately gave Cancergirl a good attitude. It was very deliberate. Since I needed people more than ever, I wanted to make sure it would be easy for them to be around me. In the end, it also made it easier to live with myself.

Cancergirl slipped away fairly quickly. After a few weeks in Cancerland, I came to terms with the fact that *she* was *me*. I had cancer, and I was still the same person. I would learn what I needed to know and do what I had to do. And I would live my life while I was doing it.

6

Cancer and the Spouse

"I'm resigning as your *porte-parole*," says Doug. The word means spokesman. He is working very hard on his French.

It's finally getting to him. After five months of patiently accepting the added responsibilities of being a cancer patient's spouse, my husband would like to restructure the role. In plain English, he would like to go to the grocery store, the health club, or a restaurant without running the gauntlet of well-wishers asking detailed questions about my health.

Maybe he needs a spokesman of his own to make an announcement: "Doug is leaving his position as Libby's spokesman to return to his first love—French. He will gladly continue to accept greetings and good wishes. Please direct lengthy, complicated cancer inquiries to Libby."

Unfortunately, I can't accept the resignation because I didn't give him this job in the first place.

PEOPLE ARE OFTEN wary about approaching the patient. They don't want to intrude, upset, presume, or they just don't know what to say. So they go to the husband, or live-in, or boyfriend, or to other family members. Fine. Better than fine, it's thoughtful and much appreciated. (It's difficult for cancer patients who don't have other people to run interference for them.) But it can get to be too much, and even though he used to joke about it, after a while Doug reached his tipping point.

Dr. Marla Shapiro's husband, Bobby Berger, has some advice for men in Doug's position. "People are always going to be asking about your wife, very few are going to say, 'And how are you?' Don't take it personally." Bobby said spouses have to develop a thick skin. He believes the longer the illness goes on, the more chance spouses have of getting depressed. What they need, he said, are a few "good buddies."

That advice is a no-brainer for women. But men are less likely to communicate their feelings. Until Bobby brought the subject up, I actually had no idea whether Doug was confiding in his friends. I hadn't given it a thought, though I should have. I did worry that he was under too much stress—in addition to my cancer, his elderly mother had reached the stage where she needed a lot more attention. I thought dealing with two medical crises simultaneously might send him over the edge. But he insisted he was coping well.

"No, I don't feel the need to pour out my heart," he told me. "Some people like to anguish over things and dramatize them. I don't." I figured he'd feel that way, but talking to a friend doesn't make someone a drama king. Doug said his approach was to accept the situation and deal with it as best he could. "Maybe it's my stiff WASP upbringing," he said with typical irony.

Doug would never have made the first move, but he may have felt better if someone he knew well had reached out to him. Men can be clueless about these things. A few months later, when our friend Larissa was diagnosed with cancer, I mentioned to Doug that he should call her husband. I thought he'd be annoyed with me for stating the obvious. Instead, he looked at me blankly. "Why?" he asked. The next morning he had to give me credit. "You were right, it's a really good thing I called," he said. "Abe is very upset." No kidding.

But men are supposed to "be strong." Abe told me he marvelled that his wife—the patient—seemed to handle things better than he did. "She can forget about it when she's doing something else. I can't," he told me. "I think about it all the time. I wake up in the middle of the night."

Another reader, David Gilmour, reports much the same reaction. While his wife, Sandra, reacted stoically, he had a difficult time. He said it was a surprise when she was diagnosed in 2003. She was called back after a mammogram, and they expected it would turn out to be a scare. But the doctor told them it was probably cancer. David remembers being fine until he walked out of the office, into the hallway. "I started sobbing, it just came over me," he said. "I was thinking I shouldn't be doing this. I'm the one who's supposed to be strong for Sandra." Instead, his wife had to comfort him, to tell him that everything would be okay. "We drove home, and as soon as we got into the garage, I started sobbing again."

John English remembers being totally surprised when his wife, Hilde, was diagnosed in 1996. John is a colleague of Doug's. He is an eminent Canadian historian and a former Member of Parliament. Hilde was a prominent lawyer and active volunteer in her community. For John, the real shock came when Hilde's lab results showed that the cancer was Stage 3—it had spread to her lymph nodes. Their doctor, a personal friend, was very blunt—at least with John. "Don't plan the funeral yet, but this is pretty bad."

Hilde lived for another ten years, and John describes that time as an emotional roller coaster. Her cancer came back in the fifth year, which was especially tough because five years is usually the point where patients believe that they are as good as cured, that their cancer is behind them. "One thing I realized in retrospect was we didn't talk about it much, partly because our son was young. Maybe that was wrong. I would say it was wrong," he said. "It's not that we denied the cancer existed. We just didn't talk about the consequences."

I met John for the first time at the visitation for Hilde, in early July 2006. Hundreds of people came to pay tribute to her. It was difficult for me, even though I'd never met her. At the time, I had just been diagnosed myself, and the doctors feared my cancer was worse than it turned out to be. I remember looking at her flower-draped casket and thinking, "That's me in ten years."

———————————

I remember the look on my father's face when my mother came home from the hospital after her mastectomy. Completely bewildered. That is my sense of how spouses feel after a breast cancer diagnosis. They don't know what to do or where to put themselves. Their wives may not be able to tell them what they need. So the men have to find their own way to make themselves useful. I remember my father's face now, as Doug and I get into the car after I receive my diagnosis. He takes my hand and says, "We'll do this together."

HAVING A SPOUSE with cancer means taking time off work and doing extra chores. Doug accompanied me to every major appointment, drove me to emergency at 2 a.m., visited me in the hospital, and sat with me during chemotherapy. He's the boss at his office, a think tank called the Canadian Institute of International Affairs, and can come and go as he pleases. But he's incredibly conscientious, and I could often sense his anxiety about being away as the hours ticked by. Still, we realized we were fortunate. Many people don't have the option of taking time when they need it.

David Gilmour did the same for his wife, but he took it one step further. "I needed somehow to take control of the situation. I was determined she would get the best care possible and I would leave no stone unturned."

David spent long hours and sleepless nights over the next few years doing extensive research on the treatments available both here in Canada and the United States.

He took Sandra to appointments in their hometown, Vancouver, and arranged for consultations in Seattle. He spoke to scores of doctors and asked thousands of questions about the disease. "She was pleased that I became her medical advocate, as it allowed her to simply concentrate on getting well. Friends and family thought I was the most incredible husband and that I went above and beyond what anyone else would have done...I never gave it a second thought...this was something I *had* to do...it was the only way I could deal with the situation." This activity helped him get over his first reaction—anger. "It was a hard time for me," he said. "It all seemed very unfair. I was also scared. I was scared that she would die and I was afraid for our kids." The children's reaction is a huge worry when one parent has cancer. David's younger son, Jesse, who was nine at the time, took it far worse than did Daniel, who was three years older. Jesse was upset and worried, and even told Sandra he was afraid she would die. At school, he was distracted, but fortunately he went to a very small school where his teachers were understanding and nurturing. Daniel asked a lot more questions but seemed less affected by it.

Bobby Berger said keeping a sense of normalcy for the kids was the hardest thing for him, all the more difficult because he had to do it while watching Marla slowly deteriorate during her treatment.

Parents are advised to keep to the regular routine. But as John English pointed out, "We let life go on normally, but it's not a normal life." John said he anaesthetized his emotions during Hilde's illness and didn't contemplate that it could be fatal. "It's like going into battle," he said. "There's a fundamental denial about that, and perhaps there's a cost to it. But the alternative is to give up."

Cancer can turn the tables on a couple, changing the way they relate to each other. In our case, there was nothing overt. But I felt more dependent on Doug than I ever had, and I hated the feeling. I tried to compensate by being as cheerful and pleasant as I could be. It wasn't phony, even though it was a conscious decision. When my mother had ovarian cancer, there were times when I dreaded seeing her because she was depressed and in pain. I didn't want Doug, or my brothers Moses and Sam, or anyone else to feel that way about seeing me.

Doug—like Bobby, David, and John—thrived on the role of supportive spouse. When we meet people who refer to my writings on breast cancer, Doug will usually chime in, "I'm the husband." He's proud of the way he handled this, and so am I. But he did get sick of talking about it. David feels different. "The cancer has been such a major part of my life that I actually like talking about it. I enjoy answering the questions, and depending on who I'm talking to, I'll often go into quite a bit of detail."

Not Doug. He loves telling the story of how two women approached him one morning. They asked after me briefly, and then proceeded to talk about him. "It's the spouse that's always forgotten in this," said one. "Yes, the spouse is also a victim here," the other agreed. Doug recalls that he couldn't get a word in edgewise. "Suddenly they were closing in on me, and I knew what was going to happen next," he laughs. That's right, horror of horrors, the encounter ended with hugs all around.

It happened more than once. One Monday morning, one of Doug's employees walked into his office, ashen-faced, and shut the door. Doug was convinced he was about to quit. That would have been a huge problem: this was a talented young man who would have been tough to replace. "I read the article," he said. "Article?" asked Doug, trying to remember what he had published recently. But this man had read my newspaper column and had come to commiserate. Just as Doug was breathing a huge sigh of relief that he wouldn't have to replace him, this man gave him another scare. "Stand up," he told Doug. "I want to give you a hug."

7

Chemotherapy

My vacation from cancer is over. While the rest of the world is going back to work and to school after Labour Day, I am checking in at the Sunnybrook Regional Cancer Centre for my first chemotherapy treatment. I have had exactly one week without a single doctor's appointment—a week to travel and spend as I pleased before this next part of the ordeal.

ACTUALLY, I had made up my mind that it wouldn't be an ordeal. I was so relieved to learn my cancer hadn't spread that I decided to treat the chemo as nothing more than a nuisance, an unpleasant clean-up operation. But as the time drew near, I began to dread it and to fret that I would be going through it for nothing.

Given that there were no signs of cancer in my lymph nodes, the doctors recommended chemo based on the size of my tumour and my age. The fact is that, even with a clear pathology report, no one can guarantee there hasn't been a microscopic spread that could turn into a recurrence several years down the road. The bigger the tumour, the more likely that this will happen. And the younger a patient is, the more time she has for a cancer to recur, so more aggressive treatment is suggested. Smaller cancers that haven't spread are treated with surgery and radiation, which is intended to prevent a recurrence in the same breast.

Both Dr. Arnaout, my surgeon, and Dr. Steven Narod of the Hereditary and Familial Breast Cancer Unit at Women's College Hospital had explained that chemotherapy was an insurance policy, that it actually helps very few people in my situation. But they both strongly advocated that I take the treatment.

I had expected my oncologist to do the same. But when I finally met Dr. Ellen Warner, I felt that she was giving me a big "out clause," a kind of silken parachute I could use to bail out on months of unpleasantness.

I had been looking forward to meeting her since we started emailing each other a month before. "When I read the story about your breast lump, I wanted to scream with frustration," Dr. Warner wrote. She explained that as a high-risk woman, I should have been receiving much more intensive screening—the kind of screening she had been providing since 1997, when she started a pilot study. "We now have over 500 women in the study and have found almost 50 cancers," she continued, explaining that most of the cancers she found were tiny and had not spread to the lymph nodes. "I certainly hope your cancer was found early and that you will sail through treatment and be well," she concluded. Now I was in her office planning that treatment, and much to my surprise she wasn't insisting that I go through with chemotherapy the way my other doctors had.

She sounded neutral as she explained the numbers. If you take a hundred women whose cancers haven't spread, and do nothing after surgery, the recurrence rate will be 25 per cent to 30 per cent. Hormone therapy will cut that number by 50 per cent, and chemotherapy will cut the result by another 20 per cent.

"It's like an end-of-season sale where they take off another 20 per cent," Dr. Warner explained. "The last discount is off the sale price, not the regular price." That means that three women out of a hundred will be helped by enduring months of poison. It was up to me to decide if I was destined to be one of the three. And for the first time, I felt I could actually say no.

"It's a huge price to pay," said Doug. "If this were a monetary insurance policy, we'd turn it down without a second thought." I settled it by asking Dr. Warner what she would do. Without a moment's hesitation, she said she would take the chemo.

The decision about which treatment to take was easier. I chose the shortest option, four cycles of AC—a combination of two drugs: Adriamycin (generic name: doxorubicin), a dark red drug that will burn like hell and damage your muscles if it somehow seeps out of the vein, and cyclophosphamide. The cycles were spaced three weeks apart, so the whole treatment would be over in three months. "That's all you need," Dr. Warner said.

She explained that I would lose my hair two or three weeks into the chemotherapy treatment and stay bald for six months. "I suppose I will lose my appetite and drop some weight," I asked hopefully. Like most women, I'd be delighted to lose a few pounds if I could do it without giving up anything. Maybe this would be the one positive result of chemo.

"That's a myth," Dr. Warner said, looking at me squarely. "When you're getting breast cancer treatment, you're more likely to gain weight than lose it. And by the way, gaining weight is very bad, don't do it." She said I would be prone to gaining weight because the drugs slow the metabolism but that I could avoid this by maintaining my exercise regimen. I certainly intended to ... if I could. She explained that weight gain is harmful because my type of cancer feeds off estrogen, and that in post-menopausal women, excess fat is converted into estrogen.

Post-menopausal? I had to look around the room to see whom she might be referring to. Not me! But there was more. The chemo would throw me into menopause, presumably unleashing a whole other set of delightful symptoms.

It was the final insult. Dr. Warner could sense my hesitation. "We can take you on September 5," she said firmly. "Don't put it off. You should start right after Labour Day."

Patients get pages upon pages of handouts that detail all the possible side effects of chemotherapy and how to deal with them. Doctors and nurses explain them again and again. They urge us to call with any problems or questions. They call to check on us. But before you start chemo, you need more instruction. So I was off to chemo class. I was looking forward to it, hoping I would meet some special chemo chums here.

There were ten of us in a large auditorium, two groups of three, presumably families, and four scattered singles including me. Ellie, a chemotherapy nurse, gave a PowerPoint presentation and showed a video that could have used a bit more production value. There was no chitchat. Everyone looked scared, and a man sitting a few seats away from me was crying. Hardly an auspicious beginning.

The day of my treatment didn't start well either.

"Do you know that you're anemic?" Dr. Warner had asked me during our first meeting. "Of course," I answered with a straight face. Oops! My doctor had told me that last winter. I took iron pills for about a week, and promptly forgot about it. Dr. Warner had prescribed a series of three iron transfusions.

Because of my anemia, I had to come early the day of my treatment for a two-hour iron transfusion. The first attempt to put an intravenous line into me was painful— and unsuccessful. Then I spotted Kathy, the nurse who had been able to give me a comfortable IV when I had my second surgery, at the end of July. She found a big, juicy vein and assured me that I wouldn't need to be implanted with a permanent device to receive the drugs.

With the iron transfusion, I was late getting to the chemotherapy unit and wasn't able to leave the recommended full hour between taking an anti-nausea pill and starting the treatment. As soon as Ellie, the nurse, began running the drug, I started to heave. She pulled it out, gave me a few minutes, and thankfully the rest went well. Actually, it was boring.

My friend Madeline had warned me that chemotherapy would leave me feeling blitzed. She was right. But I had an important date right afterwards. My brother Moses had just taken over a radio station, Classical 96.3 FM, and was holding a reception for the staff that afternoon. I wanted to be there. I'd never met his new colleagues, so I also wanted to make a good impression. I was hoping for the best when I noticed a big poster on my way out of the hospital. It was a pitch for patients to volunteer for a research study on how chemotherapy affects memory, concentration, and thinking ability. In big bold letters it asked the question: Does chemo leave your mind feeling kind of foggy?

I'm halfway there. Two of my four chemotherapy sessions are already behind me. So far, the worst of it is a few days of general yuckiness, a feeling of impending nausea. But there are lots of days when I feel so good I feel like a fraud. It must be the drugs.

IT'S A THREE-WEEK PERIOD. The yucky part comes first, and lasts for about a week. In the first week after the first treatment, my appetite was minimal, and I lost a few pounds. After the second treatment, I was hungry as hell, but only for specific things. Mostly, I craved protein—large hunks of meat—as well as vegetables and pasta. I couldn't look at things I normally love—like fish, alcohol, and sweets.

By week two of the cycle my eating and drinking habits would get closer to normal. But even though I felt better, the second week was the low week, the time when my white blood cell count was at its lowest, and I was very susceptible to infection. I had to avoid crowds, and leave immediately if I spotted someone sick within sneezing distance. During the low week after my first treatment, I was plagued with half-a-dozen nuisance ailments. I had a sore throat, swollen gums, cold sores, and a sty in my eye. I even broke out in pimples. The second and third times, I did better. Again, I owed it all to pharmaceuticals, and my drug plan.

One of the keys to successful chemotherapy is getting the treatment on time. But the oncologist will go ahead only if a patient's blood counts are high enough. That's why the chemo ritual begins with blood work and a wait for the results. When I arrived for my second treatment, I wanted to speed up the process by taking my first anti-nausea pill before the lab report was ready. "That would be a waste," snapped the nurse. "If the doctor delays your treatment, you've just swallowed twenty bucks."

My test showed that three out of fifteen markers were just a touch low. Rather than postponing the session, Dr. Warner told me to come back the next day for a shot of something called Neulasta (generic name: PEG-filgrastim), a drug that boosts white blood cells. I'd seen ads for it on U.S. television. It's a new one-shot version of an older drug, Neupogen (generic name: filgrastim), which has to be injected every day for ten days. When I picked it up at the pharmacy, I paid the usual five-dollar copayment. The cost to my insurance company: $2,561. When I first looked at the receipt, I thought there must be a mistake. That much money for one injection! I realized how lucky I was to have drug coverage. But the pharmacist suggested I may not be that lucky. He advised me to check if there was a limit on my plan. It turned out there was, and I would have to find another way to pay for part of my second and all of my third Neulasta shots.

I was looking forward to the week before chemo number three. I had felt fabulous at that point in the last cycle, again thanks to the drugs. And the iron transfusions. After one, I had more energy than I'd had in months, if not years.

Thanks to all the new drugs, chemotherapy is for most people not the nightmare it was just a few short years ago. Both my parents had cancer in the early 1990s. The treatments made them so sick that they doubted the extra time it bought them was worth it. "Why do they keep pushing this chemo?" my mother would ask. "So you can live in misery a few months longer?"

It seems like only yesterday that six months was the minimum length for a course of treatment. I would be finished in three. I realized I was fortunate. I kept meeting people who had longer chemo regimens, given at closer intervals, with tougher drugs. Before I started, I was warned that the cocktail I was getting was nicknamed the Red Devil. I was starting to wonder whether it was actually chemo lite—when the side effects hit me.

———————————

Twenty-dollar pills or not, I feel nauseated as soon as I'm in the same room as that stuff. All I have to do is look at the dark red fluid in the IV bag and I start feeling sick. "It's anticipatory nausea," says my chemo nurse, Ellie. "You should take Ativan."

THAT TURNED OUT to be a bad idea. Ativan (generic name: lorazepam), a tranquilizer, may have relaxed me as the red drug dripped through my veins, but it didn't help when I had an allergic reaction to the chemo. Suddenly, my arm turned red and itchy. I had been warned this could happen at any time. It's the reason patients come with a driver or have someone on standby to take them home. If you react to the drugs, you need an intravenous antihistamine. Taken on top of a tranquilizer, it knocked me out. I could barely walk when I woke up, and I had to go to bed for the rest of the day.

Still, it hardly seemed like a big deal. One drug neutralized a potentially disastrous allergic reaction, other drugs staved off days of misery and nausea, while a third variety prevented infections that could be catastrophic. Compared to the treatment my mother and father had endured—my father died of lymphoma—this indeed seemed like chemo lite.

I had to take a little credit. There were things I was doing to help myself, especially exercise. Studies show that exercise improves the outcomes for breast cancer patients. It certainly lessens some of the worst side effects—fatigue and constipation. I didn't miss a day. I played doubles tennis the morning after my first treatment. A dozen of us have a regular game, and as soon as I walked onto the court, my friend Cheryl announced, "She just had her first chemotherapy yesterday." Everyone gathered round, congratulating me for showing up. After a few minutes Jennifer looked at me with a smile and said, "Okay, that's enough being nice to you, now we're going to beat you!"

The game worried me. My heart rate went up much more than usual, and I got a lot hotter. "It's like exercising with the flu," said Dr. Warner, "don't worry about it, you're not doing damage." So I persevered, and the symptoms disappeared after the first ten days.

Dr. Warner is fanatical about exercise. She asked me about it during our second appointment. "I've been playing tennis four or five times a week," I told her, "but I still haven't gone back to the gym for weight training." I leaned forward, waiting to be showered with praise. "Go back to the gym," she said. "It'll do you some good."

Some friends are holding the first of two post-chemo dinners for me this weekend, and I am going on a post-chemo holiday with Doug at the end of the month. The prospect of finishing my chemotherapy makes me think of the genie in that old Bugs Bunny cartoon. He makes a big fuss every time he pops out of the lamp, yelling, "I'm here. Let the bells ring out and the banners fly!"

ACTUALLY, they do ring a bell for patients ending chemotherapy at Princess Margaret Hospital. It's a ten-inch brass number fixed on the wall by the entrance leading from the waiting room to the chemo unit. It was the staff's idea to mark this significant step. It's a lovely gesture, which I'd been hearing about for months. So I was a bit jealous because they don't have one at Sunnybrook. As it turned out, however, when the nurse took my chemo IV out for the fourth and last time, I didn't feel much like celebrating. I felt down, and I'm sure that was a disappointment to my family and friends.

Some people feel almost paralyzed when chemotherapy ends. "There's no structure until the next appointment, and that worries a lot of people. They think they should be doing something," said Anita McGowan, who counselled me and talked me through many of these decisions. Anita was an oncology nurse at Sunnybrook for thirteen years before joining CAREpath, and she had a constant stream of post-chemo patients who would drop in to see her. "They really needed to talk, and there's no provision for that in the treatment schedule."

Personally, much as I like the people there, I couldn't imagine going to Sunnybrook unless I had to. I wanted to enjoy the few weeks before the next stage of my treatment would begin. I had every reason to celebrate now, not that I ever need an excuse for a party. But at the end of my chemotherapy, I wasn't in the mood. As Anita said, "This is really a time to heal. It's a time for introspection."

I couldn't chalk it up to that letdown when the appointments stop, because in my case, they didn't stop. Since I carry one of the breast cancer gene mutations, doctors had already started trying to reduce my risk of a future cancer, even though they hadn't finished treating this one. Every day I came home to find messages about appointments with new specialists. It was a reminder that it wasn't over yet, just the end of one phase—and not necessarily the worst one. The problem was that everyone around me had been in party mode since the needle came out of my arm.

There was a big party right after my last treatment. Not for me, mind you. The Scotiabank Giller Prize is awarded annually to the best English-language Canadian novel. It is one of my favourite events, and I wasn't about to let chemo keep me from being there. In the afternoon, I brushed off well-wishers so I could get home and nap before the big night. By the time I got to the pre-dinner cocktail party, I thought I deserved a prize myself, just for pulling together my makeup, my outfit, and my game face.

"You must be thrilled this is over," said one person after another. "You must be elated."

"I will be in another two weeks or so," I kept saying, which was the honest truth. But first, I explained, I have to get through the post-chemo blahs, the fatigue, and the week when my blood count drops. But no one wanted to hear that. So I took to smiling brightly and agreeing that ending chemo was a great feeling.

"Everyone is so attuned to chemotherapy. When it's finished, they think it's over," said my friend Christine, who had finished chemo in July 2006 and radiation at the end of August. "But it's not over, and you don't go back to normal, at least not the old normal. If anything, there's a new normal, and it takes a while to get used to that."

Christine said the side effects of the drug she's been on since her treatment ended are worse than chemo and radiation combined. She's on an aromatase inhibitor called Arimidex (generic name: anastrozole), which is designed to prevent the production of any estrogen. It is causing urinary tract infections, terrible night sweats, and is depriving her of sleep. She has to take it for at least five years. As she described this to me, I was silently thankful I was not a candidate for this therapy. "People are hugely sympathetic when you're going through chemotherapy," she said, "but no one understands about this stuff."

Dr. Warner handed me a prescription for tamoxifen during my last chemo appointment. "Everyone's different," she said when I asked about the side effects. "Start taking this in three weeks." I was sorely tempted to forget, at least for a while, even though I knew this drug was far more effective than chemotherapy in preventing a recurrence of cancer.

8

The Hair Thing

My hair will start falling out any time after next Tuesday, so I am organizing a wig this week. The prospect of losing my hair doesn't upset me, at least not yet. In fact, I'm looking forward to wig shopping, thinking I may take the opportunity to improve on nature and pick a style that my own hair, fine and straight, can't handle.

MY FRIEND ELSA hooked me up with Zain Haji, who runs the wig boutique at Princess Margaret Hospital. Elsa has a wholesale accessory business, and the wig boutique is one of her clients. She met Zain when he visited her showroom, coincidentally on the very day I was having surgery in July. She pounced on him.

"He's a really cool guy with a great fashion sense," she told me. "You have to see *him* first."

So I did, with Elsa in tow.

The wig boutique covers its costs only, so prices are below retail, ranging between $195 for a synthetic wig and $550 for European hair, which is considered the most suitable type for Caucasians. At other wig stores, European hair starts at $1,500.

I started with their top of the line, a human-hair wig that on its stand looked a lot like my own hair. But as soon as Zain placed it on my head, I was horrified. I could get past the matronly helmet-head look; human-hair wigs can be recut and styled. But this actually looked like a wig, and it reminded me of a *sheitl*, the wig worn by ultra-Orthodox women after marriage. They were unmistakeable in the Montreal neighbourhood where I grew up. But the *sheitl* has come a long way since then, and today you'd never guess that the hair on many an Orthodox Jewish woman's head is not her own. Not surprisingly, this community has a lock on the high-end wig business.

But this wig didn't cut it. Looking at myself in the mirror, I was reminded of times I'd immediately spotted a bad wig on someone I knew. And then felt horrified to realize I hadn't known she had cancer. I wanted none of that.

Zain explained that the wig was just out of the box, that it would settle down, and that the part could be rearranged to look more natural. I was not willing to chance it. When I asked him to remove it as fast as possible, Elsa fixed me with her I'm-telling-you-this-because-I'm-your-best-friend look.

"You have to be realistic," she said.

"Exactly," I shot back. "I want a wig that looks realistic."

The next number I tried was a synthetic wig, cut in an edgy bob. Synthetic wigs are wash and wear, while human hair has to be restyled after each washing. (That usually means a trip to the hairdresser because it's hard for amateurs to blow-dry wigs.)

It looked better, a lot better. Zain explained that synthetic wigs had improved dramatically in recent years. "It's all you need if you're going to be wearing it for only a few months," he said. "And it's easier to care for. That's important while you're going through chemotherapy."

Another big advantage was the price. This wig was $337.50. And then there was Elsa's ringing endorsement: "I can't begin to tell you how *not* bad that is," she enthused.

But since I was here, I decided to indulge a little fantasy. I've always wanted to be a redhead, or at least to try it. When I told Doug about it, he confessed he's always lusted after redheads. This was news to me. Every woman I'd seen him salivate over had been a blonde. It's nice to discover new things about a spouse. But my hopes of kindling romance in red were soon dashed. It didn't look good on me. The closest to red I could get was a brown with auburn highlights. I tried a short wig that looked great, but it completely transformed me. My friends wouldn't recognize me in it. There was one more I had to try—long, feathery, and blonde. I burst out laughing as soon as it was on my head.

"Why are you laughing?" Elsa demanded. "It looks great! That wig takes seven years off you."

It did look great, but it was screaming *mutton dressed as lamb*. "Yes," I agreed, "but when women over a certain age wear hair this long, they're trying too hard to take seven years off."

Elsa sniffed. She has thick, curly, dark brown hair halfway down her back. She's always worn it this way, and it looks great. After her last significant birthday, she was featured in a fashion spread in one of the local newspapers. Since then, she's become a poster child for fabulous at fifty. "Your age shouldn't determine the length of your hair," she said. "That wig looks better than your own hair."

I was inclined to agree, but this was a look that required a sober second opinion. That would be Doug.

Before bringing him to the Princess Margaret boutique, however, I took Doug to Glicka's Wig Design. I had been sent there by my oncologist, Dr. Warner, because she knows Glicka's mom. I didn't know how religious Glicka would be, so I warned Doug not to shake her hand unless she offered it first. I was expecting a middle-aged woman, but Glicka was young—and pretty, and fashionably though modestly dressed. I discreetly checked out her long brown hair, which looked very natural. "Of course, I'm wearing one," she said immediately.

Glicka carries top-quality European hair only. Many less expensive human-hair wigs are made in China, but they are considered inferior because they are heavily processed. Because Chinese hair is dark, the wigs are boiled and then bleached to get a full range of colours. "By the time they get through with them, the hair is no longer human," Glicka said. She tried a few pieces on me, but they looked awful. I didn't have to tell her to take them off. The best course, she said, would be to get a custom wig.

But I wasn't prepared to spend $2,500 for a custom wig without first seeing what it would look like. So Glicka rummaged in her back room and returned with a wig that looked almost exactly like my hair, but was about two shades darker.

"I've had this so long I nearly forgot about it," she said. This wig, which would cost around $3,000 custom-made, had been made for a wealthy Orthodox woman who, when she grew tired of it, dropped it off and asked Glicka to give it to someone who needed it. But the wig was very small, and Glicka hadn't found a new owner it would fit.

"This will pinch," she warned, "but it'll give you an idea." In fact, I have a tiny head, and it fit perfectly. When it was on my head, we were amazed. It looked just like me. "If I made you a custom wig, it wouldn't turn out better," Glicka said. And even if I had been willing to spend the money, a custom wig isn't an option. They take four to six weeks to make, and I would need something in a matter of days. Glicka wanted me to take the wig, but I was uncomfortable. I could afford my own wig, and this one was intended for someone who couldn't. On the other hand, it was an amazing coincidence, finding this perfect fit. There's a Yiddish word for it—*bashert*. Fated.

Glicka suggested I could complete the circle by making a donation to a charity that gives wigs to people who can't afford them. And I could return the wig when I was finished with it, she pointed out. This seemed like an elegant solution.

There were signs that this wig was the one for me. At first I just borrowed it for a photo shoot. We had decided to let readers of my column at the *National Post* vote on my wig choice. I still had hair when the pictures were taken, but I hid it in a stocking under the wigs. After the shoot, my hair was a wreck. I couldn't wash it without ruining the beautiful job done on my face by makeup artist Susan Kirsch. So I kept the wig on when I went out to dinner in my neighbourhood that night. At the end of the evening, the waitress approached.

"Did you change your hair since the last time you were in here?" she asked.

"Just a little," I said, permitting myself a small white lie.

"Well," she replied, "it looks terrific!"

That innocent comment from someone I barely knew was a huge validation. It meant that I would never have to worry that my appearance would give away the truth about my condition. Instead of looking worse, I looked as if I had just walked out of the hairdresser's, which of course I had. I realized the wig would look like that every day, with almost no effort on my part. Bonus!

The doctors had told me it would take between two and three weeks after my first round of chemo. It's starting slowly. Every morning, I find a little hair on my pillow, and a little more in the shower. It's the ultimate bad hair experience. Never mind a day. Chemotherapy marks the start of a bad hair year. Make that years, if a cropped cut doesn't suit me.

BUT EVEN A bad hair year doesn't explain why so many women dread "the hair thing" and fix on it as the worst part of the cancer journey.

With breast cancer, both the disease and the treatment go to the heart of a woman's sexuality. First you lose part or all of your breast, then the chemo annihilates your hair. Our society has an overweening fixation with boobs—cute, perky ones. But for some reason, I hear more women fretting about the loss of their hair than about the mutilation of their mammaries. Maybe it's just because it's easier to talk about.

Dr. Mary Jane Esplen runs support groups for women who have difficulty with body image after breast cancer. She said for many, losing their hair is worse than losing a breast. Zain has found the same thing. "A lot of women feel it's much easier to hide the scars on their body," he said. "All they have to do is get dressed. But hair is such a huge part of a woman's identity, even if she covers it or wears a wig, she may feel like she's seeing someone else in the mirror."

Zain has fitted thousands of cancer patients with wigs and all manner of headgear. He gave up his partnership in a hair salon in 2000 to care full-time for his mother, who was dying of multiple myeloma. He had already volunteered with cancer support groups and done some freelance work at Princess Margaret Hospital. When a full-time job came open in their wig salon, he jumped at it. "Hair loss is so hard because it's the most public side effect of the disease," he said. "When you see a bald woman, you immediately think, cancer. It's different for a man."

Zain said that cancer-related hair loss also exposes women to a lot of questions they may not welcome. People ask after their health, with the best of intentions. The problem is that even women who want to talk don't necessarily want to talk about it all the time. "A good wig helps you control how much you focus on your illness," said Zain. "Wearing a wig can really help people when they're not doing well emotionally."

"Losing your hair also means the loss of control," said Anita, my nurse oncologist. "It is the outward expression of what the cancer is doing inside your body."

Maybe that's why my mother was so upset at the prospect of losing her hair when she was about to start chemotherapy to treat her late stage ovarian cancer. I travelled to Montreal to be with her for her first session, and she asked me to check out the hospital's wig supply as soon as she was settled and the IV was going. "I don't want to look like a bald old lady," she told me. At that point, we weren't even sure she would lose her hair. It was a fifty-fifty possibility with her particular treatment.

Her concern surprised me. She seemed to have stopped caring about most things by then. Ovarian cancer is a terrible disease, and she was in agony. She was also depressed—because of the pain, and because of my father's death just over a year and a half before. It had been months since she had bothered to colour her hair, and it was like pulling teeth to get her to the hairdresser. I was almost happy that she worried about her hair. It was a sign of life.

For most women the hair loss is just an added source of anxiety. "The hair thing is a constant reminder of what I have, and how long the road is," wrote a woman named Bonnie. She started writing to me before she went bald, telling me how much she feared it.

Soon after she started writing to me, and just before she lost her hair, I met Bonnie. Seeing her made me completely understand her distress. Bonnie had beautiful, thick hair that she had always considered one of her best features.

I didn't. Not only is my hair fine and uncooperative, I also hate styling it. What's more, I spent most of my adult life covering news on television. Any woman who does this job will tell you that hair, especially uncooperative hair, is the bane of her daily existence. I've spent countless hours outside, freezing and waiting for the wind to change direction so I could shoot on-camera stand-ups with my hair blowing away from my face instead of over it.

And losing your hair can cause career problems. One prominent business leader named Catherine was attending an out-of-town board meeting when her hair started coming out. She hadn't told her colleagues that she had cancer. "I wore my hair up for the two days because I knew if I wore it loose, I might have clumps coming out at awkward times. I wondered what the cleaning staff would think when they found large quantities of hair in the bathroom garbage can."

Like me, Bonnie waited until the last minute, then took charge and cut her hair off, instead of watching it come out in chunks.

Bonnie had an appointment for "the big buzz" about ten days after her first treatment. But the hairdresser refused to do it since the hair still looked healthy. As a result, and against all reason, Bonnie started thinking her hair might not be affected by chemo. At that point, hair would come out when she touched it, but there was only a little on her pillow every morning. Four days later, that changed. "The hair was everywhere," Bonnie wrote. "I kept vacuuming, and my husband was down on all fours cleaning it up. I know he was helping, but there seemed nothing worse than that picture. I thought I would get in the car and drive over the bridge."

For most women, the sight of a husband down on all fours cleaning would make a very pleasant picture indeed! And for my husband, the sight of me operating a vacuum cleaner would be his ultimate fantasy. But I'm afraid not even cancer has brought me to that.

In the end, it took a hair-raising shopping trip for Bonnie to accept reality. At Holt Renfrew, no less. She tried on a coat, and as soon as she took it off, she said, "I had to leave immediately....I couldn't believe what was in the collar of the coat....It was just full of my hair. I thought I might have to buy it because I was too embarrassed to return it to the salesperson." Bonnie went home thinking she'd never get through this, that it was a complete violation of her body.

Some women will go to great lengths to hang on to their locks. In the book *Cancer Vixen*, New York cartoonist Marisa Acocella Marchetto recounts that she chose a chemo regimen called CMF specifically to avoid losing her hair. My oncologist gave me the option of CMF, and I turned it down without a second thought. First of all, it's not foolproof—40 per cent of patients on this drug cocktail still end up needing wigs because their hair has thinned so drastically. It is also much longer than the regimen I did choose—six months instead of my three. I gladly traded my hair for those three chemo-free months.

To quote the late, great American columnist Mollie Ivins, describing her cancer treatment: "First they mutilate you; then they poison you; then they burn you." In contrast, hair loss is painless, reversible, and relatively easy to cover up. At least that's the way I see it.

Buying and wearing wigs was also my only opportunity to have fun with anything related to the cancer. I started out wanting to look like "myself." With one long blonde wig and one that was short and auburn, I ended up changing my look drastically from one day to the next. The *hair* thing, for me, was a *fashion* thing, and that's the way people took it. Instead of unwanted questions about my condition, I got a lot of hair queries: Which wig did I like best? What colour would I choose when my hair grew back? What length?

But it took me a while to come to that. As usual, I left shopping for my wig to the last minute, and I was just hoping to find the right one before my hair fell out.

The story of how I found the wig at Glicka's is truly magical. My editor at the *National Post*, Sarah Murdoch, puts it beautifully: "It's like a Jewish take on 'The Gift of the Magi.'" Some Orthodox Jewish readers put it another way: they dub it "the mitzvah wig."

IN JEWISH TRADITION, a mitzvah is both a good deed, and a commandment or religious rule. "What a mitzvah, to be able to receive the wig and also give to a charity of your choice," wrote a reader named Carole. "I'm of the belief that there are no such things as coincidences....This wig fits and looks great. You should choose it because there's a mitzvah attached to it." Another reader, Sharon, wrote: "Don't look at this as 'taking'—it's 'receiving.' The wig was left for someone who needs it—you need it; it even fits. Don't you see the synchronicity in this?"

I am neither religious nor superstitious. But I believe that wig had a special power. Glicka's giving me the wig was an act of charity that led to other acts of charity.

I even heard from the owner of the wig. In an email with the subject line "I think you are wearing my wig," she wrote, "It looks fabulous on you, and you would be crazy to choose anything else. I would really love for you to take the wig. It would be an honour and my exact intention in passing it on." Frankly, I was surprised when I received this email. I would have expected the donor to want to remain anonymous. I also expected her to be middle-aged. From Glicka I knew only that she was wealthy enough to change her wigs at will. But after several emails I met her for coffee and found that Yona was young enough to be my daughter. Yona agreed with Glicka that if I donated money to charity, it would balance the scales.

The idea for the *Post* readers to vote on the wigs is a bit of a lark, a riff off the craze for reality shows. With the loss of my hair looming, I am posing for pictures in four different wigs. Number 1 is synthetic, chin length, and blonde. Number 2, long, layered, and feathery. Number 3, short and brown with auburn highlights. Number 4 is an expensive, custom-made human hair wig that looks remarkably like my own hair.

THE RESPONSE WAS AMAZING. I had nearly five hundred emails in a week, including at least a dozen from old friends I hadn't seen in decades. Hundreds of readers polled their families, friends, and co-workers about how I should cover my chemo-induced pate. Friends called; people stopped me in the street.

Everyone tells me that cancer changes you, that when you emerge after the diagnosis, the treatment, and the emotional turmoil, you are a different person. Listening to my readers, I realized I would be transformed long before I reached that point, at least on the outside.

I learned some very important lessons from inviting my readers to participate. It was the first time I realized that I could do more with a wig than just cover my cancer and "pass for" my old self. I could have fun, and try new things, like making my hair short and dark.

Adopting an open and adventurous attitude to my new look was a preparation for the attitude I would need to get me through the uncharted territory of Cancerland. Equally important, embracing the lighter side of the hair thing transformed the way people related to me. By being able to talk about my hair without fear of upsetting me, they had an easy way in. It allowed them to ask about my situation—and to tell me their stories. And they certainly weren't shy about offering their opinions about how I looked.

I had advice from friends I hadn't seen in years, from women who have been through this before me, from a fashion-savvy nine-year-old named Madeleine, and from Sy Sperling, founder of the Hair Club for Men, and his wife, Susan. Sy liked the short wig but suggested a lighter colour.

"Number 3," said my friend Mary Lou, after giving me a hug. I hadn't seen her in months, and we were going to play tennis. I thought she meant we were booked on court three. I nodded and said, "I'll be there in a minute, I have to change my shoes." She said, "You don't know what I'm talking about. *Number 3*."

I enjoyed some very colourful dish about these wigs too. "Number 1 is a news anchor special," wrote a woman who signed herself Tidal. She may not have known that I spent much of my career as a news anchor and reporter— not of the helmet-headed variety, I hope! Tidal had more to say: "Number 2 (the long wig) looks like a trashy suburban mom, and number 3 (the short wig) is a guarantee of no sex—ever again."

I disagreed on that last point. Doug had been with me when I tried on the wigs. His eyes lit up when I pointed out that number 3 made me unrecognizable. It was definitely giving him ideas. What can I say; we've been married a long time.

Then there were the movie star comparisons. Number 1, according to Abigail, looked like Tori Spelling. Okay, she was right, and I wouldn't want that. But Abigail and a few others trashed number 4 (mid-length, blunt cut) because it was "Allison Janney on *The West Wing*, so *yesterday*." Someone else said number 2 was early Sharon Stone. Were these supposed to be insults?

Susan provided the most novel reason for not choosing number 3. She pointed out that it looked like the one worn by the character Samantha (played by Kim Cattrall) in *Sex and the City* when she was stalking her boyfriend to see if he was cheating. I must have missed that episode. On the show, Samantha ended up getting breast cancer. Then she wore a different wig every day.

Which leads me to the question everyone asked: which one was the Glicka wig? It was number 4; it was also the first runner-up in the wig contest, with ninety-one votes. The least favourite wig was the long one, number 2, the one I had described as mutton dressed as lamb. It got only twenty-four votes. Number 1, the fuller bob, got forty-one yeas. But the overwhelming favourite was the short brown one, number 3, with 243 votes!

A few readers gave me the kind of shopping advice I am very open to: "Take them both."

In the end, I decided to buy the short auburn wig for fun, though I was not sure I could carry it off without a full face of makeup. I also gratefully accepted the wig from Glicka.

Dr. Warner and Glicka's mom both participate in a charity bike ride to raise money for a non-denominational children's orthopedic rehab hospital in Israel, the Alyn Hospital. I decided it was appropriate to give a portion of my wig donation to that cause. I told Dr. Warner I would give the rest of the cash to a wig assistance fund at another hospital, though I would have given it to Sunnybrook if there had been something comparable there.

Dr. Warner was back to me in a flash. She told me the chemo unit at Sunnybrook kept a stash of "rather ghastly wigs" for needy women and that it had never occurred to her to start a fund for women who can't afford wigs. "What a fabulous idea!" she enthused. "We're starting one right now through the Sunnybrook Foundation."

The process of losing my hair in big clumps actually starts one day early, on a Monday, and not with the hairs on my head. I notice my pubic hair coming out in bunches in the shower, giving me my latest cancer joke: "I have less pubic hair than a porn star!" In no time, I have none—a kind of strange surprise every time I undress in front of a mirror. So I will get a holiday from waxing. Another bonus!

THE HAIR ON MY HEAD was a bit tougher. I spent the first part of that week fretting about whether it would last until Thursday. I had an event that night, a book launch where I would be working, conducting interviews. It would be full of media people I hadn't seen for months. I felt it was important to show up at this party looking like my old self. So I figured that Murphy's Law would prevail, and Thursday would be the day I could no longer get away with my own hair. I was right.

I had asked Glicka to have the wig ready for me, just in case. But it was a few days before the Jewish High Holidays, her busiest time of year, and she couldn't guarantee it. I was to call her the day of the party if I needed it.

In the meantime I didn't wash my hair for those three days, hoping that would preserve it. That's unheard of; I usually wash my hair every day. A few hours before the event, I jumped into the shower without a cap, and sure enough, my hair came out in hunks. Talk about being overly optimistic: there I was spraying in volumizer while my hair was shedding everywhere. But when I finished, I was surprised to see that my hair still covered my head and looked okay.

Still, I was relieved that Glicka had come through for me and the wig was ready. She had taken out the combs that attached the wig to the previous owner's hair and replaced them with strips that would adhere to my scalp when I went bald. On the way to Glicka's salon, I debated asking her to just buzz off my hair so I could leave wearing the wig. By the time I arrived, I had made up my mind. During the half-hour drive, my hair had shed all over the new dress I was wearing. The front of the dress was completely covered.

But Glicka looked horrified when I asked her to do the deed. "I can if you really want me to," she told me. "But it might make me cry."

I remember feeling annoyed, thinking, "If it doesn't upset me, why should it upset you, you're the professional?" But I kept my mouth shut. Glicka was the last person I wanted to upset, and she came through with an elegant solution.

She put the wig over my hair, attaching it with bobby pins, and blended the two together. It looked great, and I didn't have to worry about shedding into the canapés. At the book launch, no one could tell. Even though my bout with breast cancer was the only thing people seemed to want to talk to me about, it was comforting to know I looked like my old self.

The next morning was another story. My hair came out in huge chunks when I tried to comb it. I covered it with a beret for a meeting at Princess Margaret Hospital. "Nice hat," said Paul Alofs, head of the Princess Margaret Hospital Foundation. I certainly wasn't trying to fool him. We were there to talk about cancer and the foundation's work at Princess Margaret.

I was in a nasty time crunch. It was the eve of the Jewish New Year, and we were having friends and family for dinner. After my meeting, I still had to shop and cook. But there was no question that, first, my hair had to go.

I had always resolved to get it buzzed before it became an embarrassment. Elsa, the friend who'd introduced me to Zain at the wig shop, had made me promise, and she said she would be there. We both understood that seriously thinning hair would make me look like a victim. Choosing when to take it all off was proactive. Mario, my regular hairdresser, had promised months before that he would do the final buzz. Elsa planned to come with me. But now that the time had come, I wasn't sure I wanted to make such a meal of it. A "last haircut" seemed an unnecessary ritual. Elsa was on her way out of town on business that morning, and I didn't really have the time to get to Mario's salon.

So, since I was going to Princess Margaret for the meeting, I called Zain in the wig boutique and told him I'd like to buy the short auburn wig in which I'd posed for pictures. "Can you buzz my hair off at the same time?" I asked. What a sweetheart. He said he would. And he could see me right after my meeting with Paul.

I was mentally ready to emerge bald. But, once again, it was not to be. "I can't use the razor on you because of hospital rules," Zain said. He pointed out that the hair I had left was still strong, so he spent his lunch hour giving me a very short, spiky haircut, painstakingly arranging the thinning pieces to cover my head. His efforts were worth it: it was one classy comb-over—Donald Trump, eat your heart out!

"Are you ready?" Zain had asked at the start. "This will be emotional for both of us."

Actually, it wasn't. At that point my hair was gross, and I just wanted it off. The last time I tried very short hair, it hadn't looked good, so my expectations were not high. I was stunned when I saw Zain's handiwork. The close crop he gave me looked fabulous! The first person I saw afterwards was my friend Michina. "That looks terrific," she said, "you should think about keeping it that way when it grows back."

But I was still worried about how my family would react, especially my brother Moses. He's not good with illness (and I'm being diplomatic here). This haircut was the first really visible sign of how the cancer was transforming me, and I was afraid it would upset him. But his eyes lit up when I answered the door: "I've always thought girls with really, really short, androgynous hair are incredibly sexy," he said. Like my husband's confession about lusting after redheads, this was news to me. Moses's partner of many years—Marilyn, who is like a sister to me—has always had beautiful long hair.

So I was loving my hair, but I knew it wouldn't last. This hairdo would have a few days of life, tops. My solution, once again, was to refrain from washing or combing it. Every morning, I gently rearranged the layers. It ended up the colour of the clay courts I play tennis on—like mud. But Doug kept insisting it looked fine. I was relying on him to tell me when it was time to take a razor to it. In retrospect, that was a bad idea. You need a girlfriend for that.

On the way back from the hospital one afternoon, I stopped in to one of my favourite shoe stores and discovered that the owner had been following my story in the *Post* very sympathetically. As she and I chatted, I noticed her eyes wandering to my temple area. So I asked her, "Is too much of my bald head showing? Is it time to shave this off?" She nodded yes, and I realized that I'd let the hair go one day too long. I was embarrassed to be caught out in public like that, although the red suede spike heels I bought took away some of the sting, at least while I was sitting down. Whether it's as a remedy for feeling blue about cancer or about something more mundane, shoe shopping never fails to work its magic for me!

This time I wasn't going to make a production out of it. I arranged to go up the street to my local nail and hair salon for my buzz cut. I took the last appointment of the day, hoping I'd be alone. No such luck, but there was only one other person in the salon, an animated woman getting a pedicure. A teenaged boy walked in and sat beside me just before the stylist was ready for me. Suddenly, I felt very uncomfortable. But I needn't have worried that people might stare. In fact, they very pointedly avoided looking. While my hair was coming off, the two other customers sat silently, with their eyes fixed firmly on their feet.

I nearly burst into tears, but that was because of their reaction, not because of my own feelings, or the way I looked. Once again, I was pleasantly surprised. I had expected to look unattractive, because my face is long and I've always thought I need volume around my temples. It turns out that my head is also round, however, and it balances the shape of my face. So I was happy with the way it looked, but I still wasn't ready to walk around bald. That would take more than a week. And once again, I unveiled my new look on a special occasion, just like a healthy person might.

––––––––––

These days my appearance is changing as quickly as my holiday table. On Rosh Hashanah, the Jewish New Year, I set the table with my mother's gold-rimmed dishes and a challah cover embroidered by my sister-in-law Marilyn. I surprised our guests when I greeted them with short, spiky hair, unlike any style I've had before. Now, on Thanksgiving, just two weeks later, I pull out the Spode china that's been in my husband's family for a century. I make a centrepiece with gourds and acorns in a wicker basket. This time, when I go to the door I am completely bald.

IT WAS A KIND of debut. I'd shaved my head ten days before, but I certainly hadn't displayed it in public. This was a festive occasion, but I was at home, and everyone joining us was very close. "You look like Sinéad O'Connor," said my friend Jodi. I gave her a hug. Actually, I looked nothing like Sinéad O'Connor. To the full-haired majority, I'm sure all bald women look alike. It's very odd. I had taken pictures of my head bald, and I was quite happy to see them published in the newspaper, but I still wouldn't appear bald in public.

Sometimes I wouldn't even walk around bald in private. The week before, a candidate in Toronto's municipal election rang the doorbell. We wanted to talk to him. Doug was changing, so I headed downstairs to answer the door. Then I realized I was bald, so I headed back upstairs to get a cap. So much time elapsed that the candidate left and we had to chase him down the street. This guy is a seasoned political operator, and I'm sure he wouldn't have batted an eye if he saw my bald pate, which was probably obvious under the hat anyway. And he was bald himself. So what was my problem?

It was that I didn't want every conversation to be about cancer. And I didn't want everyone I talked to thinking, *She has cancer.* The wigs deflected that, even if most everyone knew they were wigs.

I got used to wearing my wigs very quickly. People kept telling me I looked very good for someone in the midst of chemotherapy. I'm sure it's because the wigs, unlike my real hair, always looked perfect, and enhanced my appearance. There's another bonus: throwing on a wig is a lot faster than blow-drying your hair. I cut my getting-ready time in half. I found a wig comfortable, though the first few times I wore one for an entire day, it started to bug me by late afternoon. I looked forward to getting home and taking it off. Still, in the scheme of things, it was more comfortable than wearing high heels all day.

When I wore the longer Glicka wig, which looked like my hair used to, people asked whether I was wearing a wig or whether I hadn't lost my hair yet. When I wore the short brown wig, many gave me the thumbs up, telling me that's the one they voted for when I asked for opinions in my column.

But the wigs also got in the way of normal conversation. I forgot I was wearing the brown wig when I went to the dry cleaner's one day. I said hello to the woman behind the counter and proceeded to talk about stains. She seemed to take a long time puzzling over whether she'd be able to remove one from the elbow of my sweater. She started looking at me funny. "Libby?" she finally said. "I didn't recognize you, and nobody else did either, that's why the guys didn't say hi." Everyone in the back had looked busy when I walked in, but I hadn't thought about it. "That's a huge change," she said and continued to look at me funny. I couldn't tell if she realized I had cancer, but I wasn't in the mood to explain. It suddenly occurred to me there would be further confusion if I wore the long wig next time I came in.

I hadn't considered that problem before, but I realized I would drive myself crazy if I tried to keep track of where I appeared in each wig. So I didn't. I began to think it would be easier to walk around bald.

The worst part of wearing a wig is getting too hot, and that only happened twice. Actually, I wasn't wearing a wig, exactly. I have a little fringe thing that's like a hair band made of hair. It's meant to be worn under a hat. It makes the headgear look better, but it's kind of scratchy and nasty. I remember feeling overheated while wearing it in a café. I looked around the room and resented all the men who were sitting there quite bald without attracting any attention.

That's exactly how some breast cancer patients feel. I've received email after email from women who told me they wore wigs for other people's comfort, not their own. They said they felt liberated when they uncovered their heads in public. I intended to do the same thing. What was stopping me? Maybe I was waiting for the right occasion—an avant-garde party or a runway show—when my bald head could pass for a fashion statement rather than be a declaration on the state of my health.

That perfect occasion came up a few days before my last chemo. The fashion magazine *Flare* was throwing a big bash. Not only would the party be fashionista central, but the magazine is also very involved in breast cancer causes. It seemed perfect. Doug kept encouraging me to do it, even though he wouldn't be around to go to the party with me. I picked out a dress that would work with a bald head and then went to the hairdresser to buzz off the stray hairs that were growing back. I canvassed my fashion friends, but they seemed reluctant to tell me what to do. I emailed my host, David Hamilton, who was the magazine's publisher at the time. "Come as you wish. We'll love you, either way," he wrote back.

A few hours before the party, I saw an acquaintance who is a major player in the fashion business. "Don't go bald," he said adamantly, and I listened. He was very sweet, and seemed concerned about me. But I strongly sensed that he was repelled by my disease. I've rarely encountered that reaction. I imagine that repulsion was the usual response back in the days when the C-word was whispered. But I was more likely to run into people who were *drawn to me* because I had cancer, or at least because I had cancer and was dealing with it.

"You missed your chance," Doug said when I told him I wore a wig that night. He sounded genuinely disappointed in me. I was a little disappointed in myself, though I felt my cancer was getting enough attention without my going around bald. Attracting any more attention might have seemed gratuitous.

"Women who appear in public bald are usually making a statement," said Zain. I've always been adamant: the only statement I want on the top of my head is a fashion statement. A declaration that you can live well in spite of cancer. I used my wigs—"the girls" I like to call them— in that way.

At the beginning, I figured that the longer blonde wig would be for business, because it looked like the old me. The brown wig would be for fun, because it made me look like someone else. But as I started wearing them, I found I based my choice each morning on what I was wearing, what the weather was like, and where I was going after work. I got over fretting about what the dry cleaners would think. My colleagues quickly got used to my looking completely different from one day to the next. So did everyone else.

Some people even asked if I'd be getting more wigs. I didn't, but I changed the style on my long wig after a few months. It amused others, and it amused me. It occurs to me that the only people in our society who appear in long blonde hair one day and short dark locks the next are celebrities. Maybe that's why people responded so positively. One thing is certain, no one felt sorry for me.

I took to extolling the virtues of wigs to anyone who would listen. I doubted I would give them up even after my hair grew back. And that happened a lot faster than I imagined.

Now I know how pregnant women feel when complete strangers come up and touch their bellies. Since I unveiled my brand-new, post-chemo, baby-soft little boy's hair, my head has been public property. Everyone just wants to touch it, so that's what they do.

MY COLLEAGUE John was the first person to see me after I took off my hat on the morning I deemed my crop-top ready for the office. He knows me well enough to run his fingers through my hair, which is more than I can say for most of the people who've taken to doing that, usually without so much as a "how do you do?" It's reached the point where I feel grateful when someone asks permission first. And they don't really have to ask. As soon as I get that look—the one usually reserved for small children and pets—I just say, "Sure, go ahead."

"You look gorgeous," John said, giving my head that first prolonged pat.

Full marks to John. That is the correct response, the only correct response.

If this were a multiple-choice exam, my boss, George, would have failed. "You look like GI Jane," he said, eyeing me from my doorway. I scowled. He persisted. "It looks good...but you look like GI Jane."

Granted, the style was somewhat butch. That was one reason I hesitated about unveiling it. For weeks, my friends had been asking when I would unleash my new hair on the world. "When I wake up in the morning wanting to look like a lesbian—not that there's anything wrong with that," was my usual answer. When I wake up in the morning and like the way it looks, was what I was really thinking.

It happened a lot faster than I expected. Doug kept close tabs on the back of my head, giving me daily updates on how fast my hair was growing and how many bald bits were left. "Any day now," he kept telling me for weeks, "and you'll be able to walk around like that."

But I was in no hurry to give up "the girls." I enjoyed wearing them, and was planning on doing so at least until my hair was long enough for a style I would have chosen. And the wigs were so easy. I got into a routine of taking the girls back and forth to the gym. I'd just leave them on the vanity table in the locker room while I was working out or playing tennis. The sight of me carrying them around would make people laugh, especially kids. When my friends saw a wig before they saw me, they'd boom out in a loud voice, "Is Libby here?" I liked that.

But, later, schlepping a wig to the hospital for radiation every morning, was more of a pain. I'd have to leave it in the car or an open locker, or wear it on the radiation table and wreck the style. At that point, the deep freeze had hit Toronto, and I was wearing a big, warm hat that wouldn't fit over a wig. My solution was to cart the wig to work and put it on there. One day, I arrived late from the hospital, about half an hour before a concert was scheduled to start in our lobby at Classical 96.3 FM. Moses had by now hired me. I didn't even have a bag to cover the wig. I tried to look nonchalant as I carried my blonde head past bewildered-looking listeners lined up at our front door. Walking "the girls" may have been fun at the gym, but it hardly seemed appropriate in a public, professional environment. So I kind of lunged into my office, trying to hide the thing under my coat.

"What's wrong with her?" one colleague asked.

"I guess she doesn't want us to see her without her wig," the other answered.

That was definitely the wrong message to send. But it took a barroom conversation before I found the courage to bare my head for the world. After I lost my hair, I wore a cap that covered much but not all of my head while I was playing tennis. I would remove it as soon as I got hot. "I'm taking my hat off now," I would warn opponents who hadn't seen me like this. "Don't be alarmed, I'm bald."

It didn't seem to bother anyone, so the hat often stayed off when we afterwards repaired to the bar. No one ever mentioned it, at least not in front of me. As soon as the new growth covered my head, my friend Nick weighed in: "That hair looks incredibly sexy." He was blushing, so I figure he was telling the truth. Nick is English and went to fancy boarding schools. "It reminds me of my little boy phase," he confessed.

My head had caused a very different reaction in the same bar just a few months before. I was having a conversation with a male friend who, as it turned out, was supposed to invite Doug and me to a holiday party. His wife telephoned a few days before the event, full of apologies, when she realized the invitation hadn't been extended. "He was so upset by the sight of you in your short hair that he forgot," she told me. Of all the sorry excuses for dropping the ball, this one was actually pretty original. But you have to substitute "cancer" for "short." Seeing my cancer hair was what had upset him.

That's why I wanted to wait until I could pass for something other than a cancer patient—say, a sexually ambiguous member of the military—before taking my new 'do on the road. "You're not hiding anything, but you don't have to look like a concentration camp survivor," said hairdresser and makeup artist Steve Roy. I met Steve when he did my makeup for the bald shot in the newspaper. This time, he wanted to do more than makeup. "All we need is a little paste to make this look like a real hairstyle," he said. "You should show people how to make this stage look good."

My hair grew quite a bit in the first few weeks after I exposed it. Soon there was enough for those stylish spikes. But they required a lot of product. And with all that paste and hairspray, no one—neither strangers nor friends—wanted to run their fingers through my hair.

9

Cancer and Friends

"You find out who your friends are when you get cancer." I'm hearing that over and over again these days. But I think the truth is more complicated. First of all, most of us are in our middle years by the time we're diagnosed. We should already know who our friends are.

LIFE IS FULL of surprises, especially when you hit a rough patch, whether it's illness, a death in the family, a job loss, or divorce. Sometimes casual acquaintances really step up to the plate, while old friends can't be bothered to call. Some people deserve a little slack, others don't.

Then there's the question of whom you turn to, and when. It can become political, especially among women, where confidences are an important currency of friendship.

I decided to wait until I had a proper diagnosis before telling my brothers. And I intended to tell only my very closest friends, and only as I happened to see them. Doug and I were set to go out with our friend Vicki just hours after I was told my lump was suspicious for cancer. I told her immediately, partly because I figured she'd realize something was wrong. The next day I played tennis with Barb, so she was the next to know. I told Eithne over coffee. That was a long conversation: her practical, unsentimental approach meshes so well with my own.

After telling Eithne, I told a mutual friend, the woman who introduced us. Like me, she has a family history of breast cancer. Unlike me, she's been in a high-risk screening program for years, and she is far more vigilant. In that initial stage, she had great advice about getting into the system. Over the next few weeks, she was in constant touch with Eithne about my progress, calling me occasionally. Then I realized how hard this must be for her. I was living her worst nightmare.

I held back when Elsa phoned. Elsa is one of my oldest and dearest friends, but I couldn't deal with this on the phone. She didn't suspect a thing, she was just saying hi. "There's something I want to talk to you about, in person," I told her. It didn't look like our schedules would mesh any time soon. Finally, Elsa cajoled it out of me and immediately started to cry: "You mean you weren't going to share this with me for weeks!"

Even with a small, tight circle, it's hard to control who knows what. I had no intention of hiding my breast cancer; it would be public soon enough. I just wanted to know exactly what I was dealing with first. When Elsa checked in a few days later, she asked if I had told our friend Fern. I said I would wait and asked her to respect that. But within hours there was another call. Elsa had relayed the news to Fern: "She cares about you, and she should know," Elsa said. I started to get worked up, but before one angry word came out of my mouth, I realized she was right. It was great to hear from Fern about a nanosecond later.

The circle was widening, but in my mind this information was to be private until my first breast cancer column was published in July. Soon, someone very close to me started bringing greetings from people I barely knew—her cleaning lady, an aesthetician I stopped seeing years ago. Why was she telling these people when I hadn't yet informed many of my friends? Again, instead of getting angry, I just let it go. I was starting to learn one of the lessons of cancer. It affected my friends, and I had to let them do what they had to do to deal with it. I had to let them do things to help me, even when I didn't need help. I also had to stop sweating the small stuff.

My insistence on sharing the news face to face would come back to haunt me. Some of my close friends live out of town. I found the idea of calling to say, "Hi, I have breast cancer," unthinkable. I still do. So instead of being the bearer of bad news, I waited for my friends to find out. It was summer, and people were away or at isolated cottages when my columns came out on the weekend. I wondered when I'd hear from Monika. We are close but only get to talk every few months because she lives in a different time zone and has small children. I finally got a message from her about a month after I started writing my columns. She was sobbing into my voice mail, explaining that she'd been out of the country for a month, and couldn't believe what she was reading. I felt like a complete jerk.

Then there were the people who didn't call. I have to wonder why I give them a thought when so many others took the trouble to let me know they were thinking of me. There's a group of women I used to work with. We ate lunch together every day for more than a decade. I didn't hear from any of them, and that confirmed what I always knew: these friendships would not survive the work experience.

There are many reasons people don't call. They think you're deluged; they don't want to bother you; they feel awkward. That's why God invented email. I appreciated email: it was easier for the person who was writing, and it made it easier for me to respond when I was feeling up to it. I was most negligent with the people who took the most trouble getting in touch. I mean the ones who sent hand-written notes. In some cases, I took months to acknowledge the gesture, and even though they all said no acknowledgement was necessary, I felt it was, and I felt badly.

I also felt badly about the times I myself was neglect-ful, particularly with Dr. Marla Shapiro, CTV's medical consultant, and the author of *Life in the Balance: My*

Journey with Breast Cancer. I knew Marla, though not
well. She had been the on-air doctor at Citytv when I was
there. She came into the newsroom once a week, usually
when I was out on location, but I can recall half a dozen
conversations with her. I certainly knew her well enough
to contact her when I found out she was ill. I meant to a
dozen times, but I never did. I'm still ashamed of that.
When I was ill, we were put in touch by a mutual friend,
and Marla was extremely helpful and supportive. That, I
suppose, is another lesson about friends and cancer.

I'm a hard-core party girl, but I feel some unfamiliar anxiety as I
approach this year's round of seasonal celebrations. I know I'll be
meeting people I haven't seen since I was diagnosed. There will be
friends who don't know I have cancer, others who hadn't bothered
to get in touch, and strangers who want to share intimate details
because they've read my columns. It raises some questions Miss
Manners never pondered. How much do I have to say when I just
want a drink and a laugh? And how can I talk about cancer without
bringing down a breezy festive occasion?

MY OUTRAGEOUS friend Annie Smith is the
miracle of Princess Margaret Hospital. She was diagnosed
with breast cancer twenty years ago and developed ovarian cancer in the late 1990s. It spread to her liver, lungs,
and abdomen, and she's had every available treatment.
The phrase *beating the odds* doesn't begin to take the
measure of her survival. You'll never see Annie without a

smile on her face, and she works hard to raise money for cancer charities.

Annie is an inspiration, and I'm sure that can get tiring for her. When I ran into her at our tennis club's Christmas bash, she was in the middle of her fifth round of chemotherapy. As the room heated up, she whipped off her wig and attached it to her belt. "I'm wearing it as a codpiece," she announced.

For me, it was all about the wigs. I was mostly wearing the short dark one. People told me I looked better and younger as a brunette. (Were they saying I looked old as a blonde?) That's the conversation I called cancer lite, where we covered the issue of my health once over lightly and then moved on.

"What made you decide to go for such a big change?" one woman asked at a party just before Christmas. I was wondering why she hadn't ever said anything about my diagnosis—not because I knew her that well, but because she also had cancer. Her comment on my hair made me realize she was unaware of my condition, so I filled her in.

The breast cancer sisterhood makes for fast friendships, even though it's a club no one wants to join. I went to Eithne's Christmas party just after writing about my mastectomy versus no mastectomy dilemma. I was barely in the door when I met Barbara, who told me she has never regretted her decision several years ago to have the surgery with no reconstruction. I had to do a double take. She was wearing a sexy halter top and was very buff. "My six-year-old goes around telling people his mother only has one breast," she told me. "He seems really proud of it."

"This is the survivors' corner," she said, shooing away the guys after my friend Christine joined us. Christine was surprising us with a sneak peek at her newly regrown hair. She had finished chemo in the summer and now had a close-cropped dark 'do that looked great. "It's a weekend look," she said, reminding us how corporate her job is. "I still wear the blonde wig at the office."

On the party circuit, I also heard unwelcome news about a couple of my favourite men. Prostate cancer. Just when I was fretting about what to say to former colleagues who hadn't called or written, the shoe was on the other foot. My friend Pat had been diagnosed the previous summer, around the same time I was. For Rob, the diagnosis was fresh. Hearing about their troubles gave me a little perspective. Maybe my focus on the cosmetic results of my treatment was self-indulgent. The choices and the consequences facing men with prostate cancer can be a lot worse.

I needn't have worried that being public about my disease would make for awkward moments and maudlin cocktail conversation. If anything, it allowed others to open up. That holiday season proved we've come a long way since the C-word was whispered behind closed doors. And I didn't have to raise anything more traumatic than the colour of my hair.

Larissa is young, beautiful, and has no family history of breast cancer. Until now, she has led a charmed life. There was no cancer in
her life before I was diagnosed. I almost feel responsible—as if I
brought this into her world, as if I gave this to her. How nutty is
that?

IT WAS GETTING so I was afraid to pick up the
phone. My friend Larissa called, I thought to make a date
for us to meet, but I was wrong. Then I heard from Jeanie
for the first time in several years. And finally Linda
returned a call after three of mine. By the end of the week,
I was consumed with an irrational question: Why are all
my friends getting cancer?

I hadn't been in a hurry to call Larissa back. She lives
in Vancouver and she knew I would soon be visiting that
city. When a two-week round of phone tag finally ended,
I was in for a shock. I was finishing up radiation, and I
chattered on about my health and treatment. Eventually
she got a word in. "I have cancer too," she said. It hit me
like a body blow.

"What?"

"I have breast cancer," she repeated.

Jeanie is a casual acquaintance. I hadn't seen her in
several years. But her message, "Please call me, it's
important," set something off in the pit of my stomach. I
had no doubt why she was calling. "I nursed my husband
and my son through their final illnesses," she told me,

"but now that it's me, I can't face up to it. I'm having a really hard time." Jeanie was just recovering from her surgery and waiting to hear whether she needed chemotherapy. We agreed to meet for lunch.

Linda wanted to get together that same day. "I'm having lunch with an old friend who's just been diagnosed with breast cancer," I told her.

"I have colon cancer," she said, "and they don't know how bad it is."

Talk about being trumped. I couldn't get together with a close friend to comfort her about a cancer diagnosis because I was already meeting someone else to do the same thing!

At least I'd now figured out why Linda hadn't answered my calls and emails. Earlier that week, I bumped into her husband at the grocery store. He seemed a bit flustered and clearly not in the mood to chat. He's always shy, although I know him well, and I figured he was just in a hurry. But, in fact, Linda was trying to keep a lid on the bad news, at least until she knew exactly what the news was.

It took a few weeks before I could sit down with Jeanie, Linda, or Larissa, and in the interim I found myself worrying about them. A lot. "I feel like I'm 'cancer central,' and it's really stressing me out," I told my husband. Don't get me wrong. I'm not complaining. I strongly believe that talking to others when they are at the start of this journey is the most important thing I can do. I am deeply grateful to the women who took time to talk to me in those early days, when I was feeling devastated, frantic, and bewildered. I am happy to talk to strangers, so there's no question about being there for my friends. I would be hurt if they didn't call. But it takes its toll.

Larissa visited me when I was in the midst of chemotherapy, just after I lost my hair. She had expected to sit with me at home, possibly while I was in bed. She thought I'd be down. Instead, I had fun modelling my wigs. Then we went for lunch and a full day of shopping. Months later, after her own diagnosis, she told me: "I'm much less frightened after seeing you go through it." That helped, but only a bit.

By the time I saw Jeanie, she was in much better shape than she had been when we had talked on the phone. Even though her tumour was large, her doctors had decided against chemotherapy. "Does it make me happy? Are you kidding?" she said. The chemo was the part she'd been dreading, and now that it was off the table she was managing fine.

Linda's case turned out better than she originally feared. When we had dinner before her operation, she told me the doctors warned she might have Stage 3. "The surgeon was surgeon-y, which is to say heartless," she said. "After meeting with him, I was ready to short-circuit the entire process and just dig the hole and climb in." It turned out she had Stage 1 and didn't need any further treatment after the surgery. "I hardly feel like I had cancer," she said a few weeks later. "It was cancer lite."

Still, now that I've been through it, watching my friends get cancer is more upsetting than it would otherwise be. I'm sure of that. Maybe because it brings back the terror of first finding out. And there's also a dollop of guilt, especially if the other person's case is worse than mine. Here I am, set up as some kind of example, when my cancer turned out to be easily treated, when it may be nothing compared to what some of my friends have.

If I didn't hate the word *survivor*, I'd say it's survivor's guilt!

10

The Gene People

If I wasn't so fascinated, I'd be upset. I'm on the phone with the genetic counsellor. She is going to fit me in on her last day before vacation so we can find out whether I have one of the breast cancer gene mutations before I have my surgery. "Before you come down, I need some information about your family. We have a computer program that rates your risk," she tells me. I know almost nothing about our family's pre-war history, but almost nothing is apparently enough.

WOMEN WHO HAVE breast cancer face many options at each stage of treatment. Women who carry one of the hereditary breast and ovarian cancer genes have additional variables, and additional decisions to make. For me, the genetic implications affected every stage, from the first surgery I had six weeks after I found the lump to the final surgery I had many months later.

After my dinner with Anne-Marie, I realized I urgently had to find out whether I had one of the hereditary breast and ovarian cancer genes.

The BRCA-1 and BRCA-2 genes normally protect women against breast and other cancers. But in some people, these genes are altered. And if you carry one of these mutations, you are missing some critical proteins and are therefore three to seven times more likely to develop breast cancer than are people who do not. Depending on the particular mutation, carriers are also more likely to get ovarian, colon, and prostate cancer—men also carry the gene—as well as lymphoma and melanoma. And even after they get breast cancer once, carriers remain at a high risk of getting it again—not a recurrence, a new breast cancer. Anne-Marie had warned me that if I was gene-positive, I should consider having a bilateral mastectomy and surgery to remove my ovaries.

That eye-opening dinner with Anne-Marie was on a Wednesday, and the call from Women's College Hospital's Familial Breast Cancer Research Unit—I like to call them "the gene people"— coincidentally came in the following morning. My surgeon, Dr. Arnaout, had asked them to see me quickly. When I brought up the fact that my mother had died of ovarian cancer, Dr. Arnaout had asked, with alarm in her voice, "Are you by any chance an Ashkenazi Jew?"

I had always known that was a risk factor. In fact, Ashkenazi women are five times more likely to carry the breast cancer gene mutations than are women in the general population. And not every Ashkenazi is equal, as I found out when genetic counsellor Aletta Poll started quizzing me on the phone. When I told her that my father's family came from Latvia by way of the Austro-Hungarian Empire, she didn't respond. But my Polish mother captured her attention. The breast cancer mutations are more common in Poland.

There are three particular alterations—two in BRCA-1 and one in BRCA-2—that are most common in the Jewish population. One of these mutations is also found in Slavic populations, as well as in India, England, Brazil, and Costa Rica. The other two are almost exclusively Ashkenazi Jewish genes. (Norwegian, Dutch, Polish, and Icelandic people also have high rates of other BRCA-1 and BRCA-2 mutations.)

When Aletta began charting my family tree, I had to struggle to remember whether my mother had one sister or two. In fact, there were two: one was younger and one was married with a child. She also had two brothers. The Epelzweigs were fairly well off, moving from the town of Dubienka to Łódź, where they owned a sock factory.

When the Nazis invaded Poland, my mother was evacuated to Russia, along with the rest of the workers in the munitions factory where she worked. While I was growing up, this was virtually a taboo subject in our home. My mother always felt guilty about surviving while her entire family was wiped out.

It wasn't until after my father died that I learned some shocking details about my mother's history. One of her brothers had been a resistance fighter. The Nazis caught him and shot him in front of my grandmother, Sarah Tema.

The rest of the family probably ended up in the concentration camp Sobibor.

I know that both my grandfathers died before the war, and the rest of my parents' immediate family, except one aunt on my father's side, perished in the Holocaust.

Who else in the family had cancer? There is no way of knowing.

It is astonishing that with so little information, Aletta and her computer have so many clues about my genetic legacy. I am both sad and captivated. I am full of regret that I know so little about my own history. I should have pressed my mother to tell me more. When I was in my teens and twenties, she would occasionally give up fragments of her past, usually the story of her escape to the Soviet Union, and her romance with my father. Rarely did she mention her family. I arrived at her bedside with a tape recorder a few days before she died. "It's too late," she told me. She's gone now, and there will be no more answers. I've taken to brooding about the grandmother I never knew, never even saw a picture of. Did Sarah Tema die of the usual concentration camp horrors? Or did she also suffer from untreated breast cancer?

MY APPOINTMENT with my genetic counsellor was exhausting. It lasted two-and-a-half hours, and there were more facts and figures than I could possibly take in. I had that now-familiar feeling of information coming at me in waves, slapping me hard. When the explanation was over, Aletta drew eight vials of my blood.

My parents, Aron and Chaya, in a displaced-persons' camp, Germany, *circa* 1946.

My "before" picture, July 2005. (*George Whiteside*)

My bald picture, October 2006. (*Brent Foster, National Post*)

Wig number 1. (*Peter Redman, National Post*)

Wig number 2. (*Peter Redman, National Post*)

Wig number 3, the popular favourite, the one that inspired me to become a redhead! (*Peter Redman, National Post*)

Wig number 4, the mitzvah wig. (*Peter Redman, National Post*)

My first re-growth, a few days after I took my wigs off, February 2007.
(*Brent Foster, National Post*)

Doug and Libby, at the Giller Prize, 2003.

A family celebration, with (*l. to r.*) Sam, Libby, Moses, Marilyn, and Doug, November 2005.

She promised a result in ten days. That would be one day before my first surgery was scheduled. That was cutting it close, but it was a lot faster than usual. Normally, it takes six months to get a result.

"We can only do this for you because you're Jewish," Aletta said brightly. Breast cancer genes are made up of thousands of nucleotides. In the general population, mutations can occur in any nucleotide. So they all have to be checked. In the Jewish population, the "mistake" happens in one of only three places. That's why the test can be processed quickly. It made me think of those old Borscht Belt jokes about the Chosen People where the punchline is: "Choose somebody else!"

The breast cancer mutations were discovered in 1994 and 1995, and they account for about 5 per cent of cases. Another 5 per cent is hereditary—women who have a family history but don't have the gene. These numbers may be relatively small, but this is a population where prevention can be very effective. That's why there's so much excitement around the discovery of the genes and genetic testing. Researchers think there are many more cancer genes that have yet to be discovered. I remember reading about the testing conundrum when the news first came out. The key questions are: If you test positive, what will you do with the information? And how will it affect you psychologically?

I knew I was a likely candidate, but that was only the half of it. I realized that I was at risk because my mother was an Ashkenazi Jew who'd had breast cancer when she was quite young. I did not know that the fact that she also had ovarian cancer made it 70 per cent likely that she had the gene. I'm in the news business, and I can't understand how I missed this information. Maybe it was accidentally on purpose.

"Your mother would not have been happy about this," says my sister-in-law Marilyn. The understatement of the century. My mother would have been horrified. She would have blamed herself—the ultimate Jewish mother's guilt. I'm glad she didn't live to see me get breast cancer.

MY MOTHER USED to tell me she thought she got cancer because of what she went through during the war. I don't think she actually believed this. It was probably what she told herself to prevent herself from worrying that the same thing would happen to me. But I also didn't think it was impossible. I reasoned that even if the cancer was hereditary, I might get lucky. I might be spared. Not everyone with a family history—nor everyone with the gene—gets cancer.

All women with breast cancer face tough choices. For gene carriers, the decisions are wrenching. The main issue is whether to have surgery to remove both breasts— a radical pre-emptive strike. It would be an overstatement to say I decided against testing when I was younger. I didn't even give it serious thought. The simple reason: I never would have had my breasts removed while they were still healthy. Nor would I have taken a chemotherapy drug such as tamoxifen—one of the other preventive measures for women who test positive.

I wasn't negligent. I'd been getting mammograms since the age of thirty-five. I remember being especially nervous when I approached the age my mother had been at her diagnosis. When my films came back negative, I thought I was home free. I actually skipped my mammogram the next year. Of course, I did resume the screening. Though ironically, in the end, it missed my cancer.

There are other ways I could have benefited from the heightened screening given to gene carriers, but I wasn't aware of them at the time. I started to get a sense of this just as I was being diagnosed, when I got that long email from oncologist Dr. Ellen Warner after my first breast cancer column appeared in the paper. Dr. Warner had guessed that I was a gene carrier from two facts in that column—my mother had cancer before menopause and had died of ovarian cancer thirty years later.

In her email, Dr. Warner recounted the story of how she became involved with the treatment of gene carriers after hearing a lecture from Dr. Mary-Claire King, one of the scientists involved with the Human Genome Project. That led her to a sociologist, Dr. Kathryn Taylor, who was studying the ethical, legal, and social implications of testing healthy women for a predisposition to cancer. Dr. Taylor, in turn, referred her to Dr. Narod of the Hereditary and Familial Breast Cancer Unit at Women's College Hospital, a pioneer in the area and one of the foremost authorities on genetic breast cancer in the world. He was studying families where breast cancer was rampant and discovered that in these clans, ovarian cancer was almost as big a problem. With Dr. Narod's help, Dr. Warner set up her practice at Sunnybrook Hospital (now the Sunnybrook Regional Cancer Centre) to offer genetic testing and counselling to women who were at high risk. Later, she used MRIs to screen these women.

She told me that MRIs found 90 per cent of the cancers in this group, while mammograms and ultrasound found only 25 per cent to 30 per cent. Dr. Warner was frustrated. "How many high-risk women like you will be told that mammograms and ultrasounds are all they need to find the cancer before it's large enough for them to find it themselves?" she wrote.

I knew about Dr. Warner's high-risk screening program because a friend of mine was in it. She had urged me to join. I hadn't rejected the idea. I simply never got around to it. If my doctor had referred me, there's no question I would have gone. A few years ago, I had been in what I thought was a good screening program at another hospital. But my GP died, and I went to another doctor who sent me to the private clinic where my mammograms were eventually misread. I have to take responsibility for being cavalier. But I think some of the blame rests with that new doctor (who is no longer my doctor). My family history should have raised red flags, and she should have sent me to one of the high-risk programs that are readily available in Toronto.

My friend in Dr. Warner's program is the only person I know who takes tamoxifen prophylactically, to prevent breast cancer. Frankly, when she told me she was doing this, I thought it was crazy. I'm not alone in this view. Only 10 per cent of gene carriers go this route. My friend had to beg her doctor to put her on the drug. She does not have the gene, but others in her family do. I have always considered her to be a bit neurotic about her health. But the results speak for themselves—she is cancer-free. Had she developed anything, God forbid, it probably would have been detected when it was tiny. Meanwhile, I ended up with breast cancer that wasn't diagnosed until it was Stage 2.

A quarter of the women who have one of the genes opt for preventive bilateral mastectomies. It's a frightful, enormous decision. It's one thing to make it after long and careful consideration, quite another to do it under the pressure of a surgical deadline. But that's what I was contemplating. I hated the idea of having an "extra" surgery—that is, having a lumpectomy and recovering only to go under the knife again for a mastectomy. If I went for the mastectomy, I wanted to arrange for immediate reconstruction because I couldn't bear the idea of waking up without breasts. I had heard about the technique that uses tissue expanders under the skin, instead of the very long procedure where your own fat and skin is harvested to make breasts. Dr. Marla Shapiro, who wouldn't have had an ounce of her own fat to use, had the tissue expanders. She showed the result to me. It looked great, although there were permanent scars.

"You're not going to wake up with breasts if that's what you do," Aletta, my genetic counsellor, cautioned me. She described how it works. Doctors stretch your skin gradually by filling the expanders with fluid every two weeks, until your breasts reach the size you want. Then they do another operation to exchange the expanders for implants. That explanation only increased my resolve to get everything over with at once.

If I have the surgery now, the process will probably be complete by next spring. But if I wait and have the lumpectomy and chemotherapy beforehand, it will just delay my recovery and take that much longer before I can put this agonizing chapter behind me.

MARLA HAD WARNED me about trying to deal with too much at once. She was the one who talked me down when I started to wonder whether I should have both my breasts and my ovaries removed all at once.

My mind had been racing throughout that long meeting with Aletta, my genetic counsellor, as I anticipated what I would decide to do if I was gene-positive. I had an inkling by the end of our session. "If the doctors tell me I should have my entire breast removed, I will go for a bilateral mastectomy. But if they recommended a lumpectomy, I will leave it at that."

Aletta thought that sounded reasonable. "As this unfolds, remember that your first instinct is often the right one." That would prove to be tough advice to follow. I second-guessed myself dozens, if not hundreds, of times.

If I decided on the bilateral mastectomy, there was a practical problem. Could I change the surgery on short notice, and could I get a plastic surgeon to do the immediate reconstruction? I went into high gear. My friend Trevor, the plastic surgeon, wrote an email on my behalf to Dr. John Semple, the head of Plastic Surgery at Women's College Hospital. I was very grateful and overjoyed when Dr. Semple answered my email immediately. He, too, cautioned me about the way I was making my decision. "Often it is difficult to get enough information in the given time to feel you can make proper decisions on these matters," he wrote me. In the end, it came down to scheduling. He wasn't available when I was scheduled for surgery, or any time close to that. It was just as well.

––––––––––––––

After postponing my surgery for a week, Dr. Arnaout just told me that a committee of doctors has decided to recommend a lumpectomy. I should be overjoyed. For two weeks, I've been filled with anxiety about the possibility that I may need a mastectomy. Instead of being happy, I'm hesitating. Will a lumpectomy be the right thing if my genetic test is positive? I honestly don't know, but I'm going with the smaller surgery. It's as much because that was my first instinct as because I couldn't make the arrangements for the other option.

MANY MONTHS LATER, I realized that delaying the decision was the right thing. Dr. Warner said she's seen cases where women opt to remove both their breasts because of the psychological trauma of a breast cancer diagnosis, then regret it. "If you have any doubt at all, you're far better off going for breast conservation," she told me.

On the morning before my surgery, I rued the day I opened the question in the first place by asking for speedy test results. If I was a BRCA carrier, it was too late to do anything about it before my lumpectomy. And the prospect of surgery was stressful enough without adding the anxiety of a positive result. Aletta had said she would try to have my results before my surgery, but it wasn't an ironclad promise. I began to hope that the lab work would be delayed. But, true to her word, Aletta called, asking me to come in to meet with the famous Dr. Steven Narod.

I assumed that I wouldn't be asked to meet the man himself unless I was a gene carrier. Suddenly I felt afraid and regretted not asking anyone to come to the appointment with me. I wished I could put it off. But I should have been careful what I had wished for in the first place. I had asked for a rush on my tests, and I was about to get it. There was no backing out now.

Aletta laid out the results before Dr. Narod came in. There was good news and bad news. I had tested positive. But not for BRCA-1. I had the BRCA-2 mutation. That's the better one. It carries a lower risk of breast cancer, 50 per cent to 60 per cent, as opposed to 80 per cent for BRCA-1. The cancer that BRCA-2 carriers get is usually less aggressive than those associated with BRCA-1. On the other hand, BRCA-2 carries a higher risk of ovarian and colon cancer, and melanoma. Aletta told me I had a 40 per cent chance of getting breast cancer again, and a 20 per cent chance of developing ovarian cancer.

Dr. Narod arrived and started second-guessing Aletta's numbers. He launched into a technical explanation I realized I was supposed to understand, and then downgraded my risk of a new breast cancer to 30 per cent over twenty years. He explained that in my case the "mistake" was in the middle of the gene, not at the end, which mitigated its severity. Oh goodie, I thought, I love getting a discount.

Dr. Narod is an unusual guy—a curmudgeon with the air of an absent-minded professor, brilliant and very blunt. "Why didn't you come to us sooner?" he demanded. "At the very least, you would have received intensive screening, and we would have found your tumour when it was much smaller than it is now." At that point, before my surgery, the doctors thought my cancer was four centimetres. Thankfully, it turned out to be smaller. Dr. Narod didn't buy my explanation—that I lacked a referral from my family doctor. "Lots of people come to us on their own," he scolded. "You knew about this research and your own risk."

He explained that taking tamoxifen would cut my risk of another breast cancer in half, and that chemotherapy (for the cancer that was about to be treated) would reduce it a little more. That would leave me with just a slightly higher risk than the general population.

As for ovarian cancer, he explained that while my risk was relatively small, the outcome could be deadly. He didn't have to convince me. I watched my mother die of ovarian cancer. "Your ovaries have to come out as soon as possible," he said. "You should have done it years ago." Having my ovaries and tubes removed would also lower my risk of another breast cancer by doing more of the same work tamoxifen does—removing estrogen from my body. The surgery is called a salpingo-oophorectomy, and it's the most popular preventive measure for gene carriers. About 60 per cent have the procedure.

Then Dr. Narod told me about a trial he was thinking about setting up. He explained that when gene carriers get a second breast cancer, it usually happens in the other breast. He kept asking himself why, and concluded it may be because the breast that had the first cancer had received radiation. He was thinking about prophylactically radiating the other, cancer-free breast. "You could be patient number one," he told me.

I was dumbfounded. This was the mother of all risky options, and it was thrown at me the day before cancer surgery, an hour before I had to be at the hospital for a pre-operative test. The good news was, this meeting had been so strange and fascinating, I couldn't be upset.

We concluded I could wait until the following spring to have my ovaries removed. I would have to decide whether I wanted a bilateral mastectomy before then. That gave me about six months to think about it. But all the time in the world wouldn't make the choice any easier.

11

Radiation

No one should have to make the choices I am facing. Now that I've finished chemotherapy, I have to decide between extreme surgery and an elevated risk of getting cancer again. I have about a month to do it. Being in this position annoys me. Better annoyed than depressed, but it's still a bad attitude.

IT'S A NUMBERS GAME, but even an advanced understanding of risk assessment won't solve the problem. I have a 30 per cent chance of getting another breast cancer in the next twenty years.

There are many ways to *reduce* this risk, but only one way to get it close to zero: a bilateral mastectomy. A quarter of the women who have the breast cancer genes opt for this procedure. They do it while they're still healthy, to avoid getting cancer in the first place. I would never have done this before my diagnosis. I still find it shocking.

"The most important consideration is what type of a person you are," said Dr. Jean-Philippe Pignol, a radiation oncologist at Sunnybrook Regional Cancer Centre. "Surgery is the right choice for people who would constantly worry about getting cancer again. Those patients are the ones who are happy afterwards." Dr. Pignol has a French accent, which I always find charming, and is extremely handsome. "Personally," he said, touching his chest for emphasis, "I can't imagine cutting off part of my body and losing the sensation."

If I go for the surgery, I won't need radiation. Radiation is intended to prevent a recurrence of cancer in the same breast. Most patients who've had mastectomies don't need it. But if I use personality as the deciding factor, as Dr. Pignol suggests, I won't have the surgery. I'll go for the radiation. I'm sure I won't worry excessively if I go that route. I'm only halfway through my treatment, I'm still bald, and I haven't yet gone for a whole week without a doctor's appointment, but I already have entire days when I don't think about cancer. I simply forget.

Still, the choice is not as simple as Dr. Pignol presents it. I've been on the verge of deciding against surgery many times. I will soon start taking tamoxifen, which will cut my risk of getting another breast cancer in half, to 15 per cent. The chemo I've had will reduce that number a little more, and so will the surgery to remove my ovaries that is scheduled for next spring. I will be monitored much more closely than the average woman. So chances are, if I get cancer again, it will be caught earlier than it was this time. I can handle the possibility that this may happen. I don't think another early cancer would necessarily be more traumatic than a double mastectomy and a breast reconstruction.

There is one but, and it's a big one. If I take my chances and do get cancer again, I may need a mastectomy. If that happens after I've gone through radiation, it could compromise my chance of reconstruction. There's one thing I know for sure: mastectomy without reconstruction is the one scenario I dread.

PLASTIC SURGEONS ARE doing amazing work these days. There are two main breast reconstruction techniques: tissue expanders and tissue transfers. I prefer the expanders. After your breasts have been removed, doctors put a temporary implant under your chest muscle. It starts very small, but every two weeks they add saline liquid through a port so that your skin gradually stretches to the size you want. Then there's another surgery to replace the expanders with permanent implants. They make a nipple with a skin graft and tattoo an areola.

But this technique may not work after radiation. "Radiation can make the tissues become stiff," said Women's College Hospital plastic surgeon Dr. John Semple when I first saw him in July. "This can lead to increased complications and less than optimal cosmetic results." The bottom line was that Dr. Semple wouldn't perform this procedure after I'm radiated, which means I would have to go with the second, more invasive, reconstruction technique if I get cancer again in the same breast.

The second technique is tissue transfers. That type of operation is called a TRAM flap. Doctors harvest fat, skin, and some muscle from your abdomen or other parts of your body to make breasts. It's a long surgery: you're on the operating table for at least four to five hours. The good news is that you wake up with breasts. The bad news is that the recovery is a lot harder and longer than it is with expanders. The tissue transfer amounts to a tummy tuck, which is why some people I've consulted don't understand why I'm so averse to the idea. Call me delusional, but I think that I can still get hard abs the old-fashioned way—they're just a few personal training sessions away.

The whole thing seems like double or nothing to me. Either I keep all my parts and everything is fine, or I get cancer again and end up needing the surgery I avoided, including the more difficult reconstruction. I was about to lay my bet and went back to see Dr. Semple. "Let me see your stomach," he said after we talked. A peek at my midriff was all he needed. "That gall bladder scar will get in the way of a TRAM flap procedure," he told me. "You're not a candidate."

———————————

After months of weighing the pros and cons, I cannot bring myself to have my breasts removed. But I can't make a firm decision against the surgery either.

THERE WAS NO eureka moment, not even a moment of certainty. Instead of making a conscious choice, I started making plans that didn't include recovering from major surgery. I started telling people I "probably" wouldn't go ahead with the procedure. Then I kept my appointment to plan radiation, a treatment I wouldn't need if I had a bilateral mastectomy.

The tipping point was my consultation with Dr. Joan Lipa, a gifted young surgeon who specializes in reconstructing breasts. She told me she could use some new techniques to reconstruct me even after radiation. That reassurance let me go with my gut: that radical surgery wasn't for me. I would go with radiation. But with all this to think about, I was worrying a lot about the effects of the radiation.

"It's a piece of cake compared to chemo," said Tanya, the nurse oncologist who works with Dr. Pignol. She was explaining the side effects, with the proviso that many people experience nothing. But I wasn't worried about fatigue and skin irritation, I was thinking about the long-term damage to my tissues. I was very worried after Dr. Semple's explanation about how radiation can complicate or ruin the results of plastic surgery.

"I want to do everything possible to ensure that I'll be able to get a breast reconstruction if I need one down the road," I told Dr. Pignol. From my point of view, that meant as little radiation as possible. It meant less treatment than he wanted to give me. Back in August, he had recommended a total of twenty-two treatments. Since then, I'd met several women who'd had shorter courses of radiation. I wanted what they were having.

Of course I understand that treatment-envy is the bane of a doctor's existence. Every case is different and so is every cure. But whenever cancer patients read about medical advances or talk to their friends about new therapies, the question is the same: Why can't I have that?

Dr. Pignol had already turned me down for his own cutting-edge treatment. (I can't remember why I didn't qualify for that trial.) He's a pioneer in the use of radioactive seeds, a one-time procedure where doctors insert needles loaded with small titanium seeds that deliver radiation continuously for two months. They don't have to be removed afterwards.

Now I was intrigued by my friend Margie's radiotherapy. Instead of twenty-two treatments—five days a week, for more than a month—she was finished after one week, with radiation twice a day. "I heard about this clinical trial at Princess Margaret Hospital," she explained. "It's still experimental, but I don't have a problem with that." I didn't have a problem with it either. I liked the idea of being on the cutting edge and getting the very latest treatment.

Doctors are always trying to figure out how to do the most good with the least invasive treatment. That's what this trial was about. Called RAPID: Randomized Trial of Accelerated Partial Breast Irradiation, it was designed to find out whether radiating part of the breast is as effective as radiating the entire breast.

Not only was Margie getting less radiation, she was getting her life back after a week. One of the biggest problems with radiation is that the daily dose disrupts your life. It can be particularly devastating for patients from out of town. It seemed to me that Margie was getting a great deal. Granted, she's about fifteen years older than I am, and her cancer was smaller—two reasons doctors would normally recommend less treatment for her.

Dr. Pignol heard me out, but he was skeptical. "We're not convinced it's really safe," he said. There was the question of whether radiation to about half the breast would prevent a recurrence. That's what the trial was testing. Then there was the technique itself. Apparently, it required a lot more skill and precision than regular full breast radiation did.

Next I asked about another accelerated radiation protocol, and Dr. Pignol left the room. "He's probably checking things on the computer right now," said Tanya. "Whatever he recommends will be the best thing for you." I wasn't challenging my doctor's authority or his expertise. I relied on him to suggest what was best. But it was up to me to check out all the options.

Dr. Pignol did more than surf the Net when he was out of the room. "I did an informal consultation with the other doctors here, and we all agree," he said. Since I have the breast cancer gene, and I am relatively young, they wanted to go with the original game plan: fifteen treatments to the entire breast and seven "booster" treatments to the area of the scar.

"I can still send you to Princess Margaret for the trial if you really want me to," he said. I was astonished that he was leaving the option open. But being an assertive patient is a double-edged sword. You can talk your way into the very latest and greatest treatment, or you can insist on something that's clearly not in your best interest. I wasn't going to do either. I was going to take Dr. Pignol's advice.

Two down, nineteen to go. I have started my radiation treatments at Sunnybrook Regional Cancer Centre. I had a longer than usual break between chemo and radiation because of the Christmas holidays, and maybe because of the backlog of cancer patients. I don't know. I certainly didn't push to get in any sooner.

"TWO-AND-A-HALF months between chemo and radiation?" Another doctor I know was appalled by the time lapse. But I was confident my oncologists would have scheduled me sooner if it had been medically necessary. The hiatus gave me more time to make the big decision. By the time I started radiation, I was comfortable with my decision not to have a bilateral mastectomy. So far, the only problem with waiting was that I hit the winter weather, and it doubled my driving time to and from the hospital.

They have it down to a science. After the first session, you don't even have to check in with the desk, as I did for every other type of appointment. It's automated: you just swipe your health card on a terminal. Every time I did that, I was grateful for our socialized medical system. I didn't want to think about how much money would be coming out each time if it was hooked up to my account, not the government's.

At the planning session, Dr. Pignol had put a kind of tracing paper over my breast and taken measurements to determine the correct angles for aiming the radiation beams and the proper dose of radiation. Then he marked me up with Magic Marker—green Magic Marker. I felt like an art project. Afterwards, I got my tattoos, three tiny dots that would allow the technicians to line me up to the machine. Those would be permanent. I had fretted a bit about the idea of tattoos on my chest, but I couldn't even find them.

The tattoos are just a guide. The radiation therapists had to freshen the larger ink markings every day before giving me my daily dose. I would laugh and pick my preferred colour, but there is something degrading about being drawn on.

Every day I arrived and parked on the lower level so I could enter by the basement door and avoid walking outside in the cold as much as possible. I turned left and then right, and walked the long tunnel from the main building to the cancer centre, landing finally in the large, open radiation waiting room. I swiped my card and checked the overhead digital display board to see if there were delays on my machine. I had been assigned to PPR 2. I would be treated on that machine for the first seventeen treatments, and then I would move to another machine for the five booster treatments to the area of my scar. I waited to be called. Then I changed, leaving my clothes in an open locker. I put on two hospital gowns, the first one opening in the back, and another on top opening in the front. Then I waited some more until I was called.

The radiation therapists who took care of me were all lovely. But, call me a big prude, I was shocked to find a man on my team when I arrived for my first treatment.

They undress you in stages. They asked me to take off one of the two hospital gowns, and then they loosened the other as I got settled on the table attached to the huge radiation machine. At this point, they started lining up the machine. I call it "radiation talk." They would recite numbers to each other and tell me to ignore them. The machine started moving into place. They were about to slip the remaining gown off my shoulders. That's when I stopped the proceedings.

"Do I have to do this in front of a man?" I asked in my meekest voice. He was very gracious. "No problem," he said, leaving the room. The ladies warned me there was no problem that day, or the day after, but if they were short-staffed, they wouldn't be able to accommodate me. I consider myself fairly uninhibited. But there is a certain amount of humiliation involved in all of this. I wasn't about to flash my post-lumpectomy breast in front of any man who wasn't my doctor.

Finally, they pulled down the left side of the gown, redrew the markings on my breast, and positioned my arm behind my head. When we first settled on this position, they warned me to make sure it was comfortable. This was the pose I'd have to assume every time, and once I was in place, there would be no moving until the treatment was over. Of course, this was usually the time when I would get an itch.

I'm halfway done, and I'm finally getting used to it. It's a large machine, and it moves into place like a noisy robot as you lie there. Then comes the most disconcerting part. When everything is ready, the warning bell starts. Beep! Beep! Beep!—it's the signal for the technicians to leave the room. These high-energy beams are supposed to cure me, but they're dangerous. "We'll be right back," the therapists say brightly as they exit. Two minutes later, it's all over, until the next day. My last radiation treatment will be Friday, February 23, and while I'm not quite counting the days, I'm really looking forward to the end.

I BECAME ACCUSTOMED to the routine of schlepping up to Sunnybrook every day. During my first week, everything ran like clockwork. I was usually in and out in less than an hour. After that, there were problems and delays. One morning the computer that runs the machines didn't work, and everything backed up for more than two hours. I felt badly for the staff. They had to work extra-long hours dealing with overflowing waiting rooms full of cranky cancer patients.

I was lucky with side effects. After the first few treatments, I thought I was getting a bad burn, but that subsided. The doctor confirmed it was unlikely I would have more than a mild skin reaction. I was also worried about fatigue, which is usually cited as a common side effect of radiation. During chemotherapy, I had put a lot of flex into my schedule in case I didn't feel well. After the chemo went so well, I took on all kinds of commitments. If I became fatigued during radiation, it would have been tough luck.

I was worried that was happening when I found I needed a midday nap a few times one week. Despite everything I'd read about radiation and fatigue, when I next saw Dr. Pignol for my weekly appointment, he told me there was no reason to get overly tired, unless I was depressed. "I am *not* depressed," I told him. After that I felt a lot peppier. It's amazing how much is in your head!

The end was anti-climactic, as these things often are. I nearly fell asleep during the forty-five-minute wait to get on the machine for my last treatment. That was longer than average, but only a bit. The waiting was the biggest reason I was thrilled this daily grind was over. It had carved a huge hunk out of my days, and I was anxious to get control of my time again.

"What are you going to do with all your free time?" the receptionist asked with a smile. She had a good sense of humour. I was totally overextended and overbooked.

"Are you going to party?" asked one of the radiation therapists. I hadn't planned on it, but it turned out that we did. My husband and I had opera tickets that night, but we left at intermission to join some family and friends at a great Brazilian club. No, they weren't there to fete me; the timing of the night out was coincidental. It was a fun place with all the meat you could eat and a Brazilian mass band preparing for carnival. "I just finished radiation today," I said, before heading out for a turn with the samba dancers. I outlasted all the healthy people on the floor.

"It's inspirational," said one of my friends, giving me an admiring look. I'm not sure what to make of it when people say things like that. I have always liked a party. The cancer has made me determined to enjoy my life even more. That's a good thing, but I'm not exactly sure it's a virtue.

12

Cancer and Work

"I'd like to write about it. Do you think it's a good idea?"

We're in our backyard—me, Doug, brother Moses, sister-in-law Marilyn, and brother Sam, who is in from Vancouver. We've been together all week for the ideaCity conference that Moses hosts, but I didn't tell them about my diagnosis until the event was over, yesterday. Today they're here eating lox and bagels, looking kind of shocked. We make small talk for half an hour before Moses abruptly breaks in. "Okay, let's talk about it." I tell them about my options and treatment. My work is the last thing on the agenda.

Chronicling my experience with cancer seems like an obvious thing to do, but I'm worried about how it will affect my career. I'm already in between jobs—which is bad enough for a middle-aged woman in the television business. I'm afraid going public about cancer will make me unemployable. I know I have to focus on getting well. But I keep brooding about how I will get back on track when this is over.

I REALIZED WORRYING about work was in itself a luxury. I was concerned about my career, while many cancer patients have to worry about more basic things, like putting food on the table. Hardest hit are people with limited resources, little savings, few health-care benefits, debts, and families to support. Families with two incomes have to make do with one, and families with one—the cancer patient's—have to scramble.

Less severe, but still real, is the hardship to professionals, especially if they're self-employed. Doctors, for instance, can't work while they are undergoing chemotherapy because the risk of catching something from a patient is too great. One of my friends, a psychiatrist, was on a once-a-week chemo regimen for colon cancer when I thoughtlessly asked his wife for a donation to a charity for which I was raising money. I was shocked to hear about the expenses that continue—maintaining the office and bringing in replacement doctors are just two examples—while the patient can't work. Another problem is the interruption in the practice. Dr. Marla Shapiro wrote about feeling that she had lost her identity because she was unable to see patients during her treatment. The good news about being self-employed, though, is that when your treatment is finished, you can just pick up where you left off.

The problems for employees can be worse, as I learned from a reader who shared the details of her case.

Her former employer had fired her without cause, two weeks after her lumpectomy. By the time she contacted me, it was nearly a year after the fact, and her family, which relied on two salaries, had to survive on one while she was ill. She wrote: "It made my breast cancer journey all the more horrific and stressful....On top of all my other fears, I had to hire a lawyer, and be concerned about where my income was going to come from." She didn't reach a settlement and receive the much-needed cash payment until the crisis was long past. With that behind her, she had to start looking for work, a process that presented a whole new set of challenges.

Time gaps don't look good on a resumé. Any potential employer will ask why you were off work. If the reason is cancer, how will that affect your chances? Any boss will have to wonder whether you'll need more time off work and end up costing the company more money than would an employee who is cancer-free.

Beyond the bread-and-butter issues and the career angst are the choices about balancing work and family, and those choices are starkest when the prognosis is not good. There was a firestorm of criticism in March 2007 when U.S. presidential candidate John Edwards and his wife, Elizabeth, decided to carry on campaigning even though her breast cancer had returned in an incurable form. "I think he should be there to support her and not out on the campaign trail," said one woman in a typical criticism. The question at the heart of the debate was: What would you do if your spouse was diagnosed with terminal cancer?

America's response was highly judgmental. The perception was that Edwards was putting personal ambition above family—even in a life-and-death situation.

Elizabeth Edwards was "surprised and disappointed. What bothers me is that they're not just saying something negative about us...," she said in a television appearance, "but they're also saying it to families who decide they're going to stay in their jobs, they're going to continue teaching, or continue painting, or continue whatever their life work is, the thing that helps define who they are."

The way Elizabeth saw it, it was a matter of "living until you die," instead of going home to die. It was also a question of what she would leave behind. "I don't want my legacy to be that I pulled somebody who ought to be president out of the race," she said. "It's not fair to me, in a sense."

Former Member of Parliament John English said he wouldn't presume to judge the Edwards' decision, even though he made a very different choice after his wife, Hilde, was diagnosed in 1996. He recalls a very frank talk with then Prime Minister Jean Chrétien. "I asked, 'Are you going to call an election? It's terrible timing for me.' He was very good. He told me, 'Yes I am.'"

It was early February 1997, and Hilde had started chemotherapy. John decided he couldn't go through an election in the midst of all that, so he gave up his seat, even though he was already nominated. Did he feel it was a big sacrifice? "Not particularly," he said. "I had a good career otherwise, and there were other reasons—like four parents in their eighties—to go back to academe."

The cancer prompted Hilde gradually to make choices about her career. She moved away from her work as a lawyer into more volunteer activity. "You cling to those things that matter and don't waste time on stuff that doesn't," said John. As a couple, they ended up travelling more and saving less money for the future. They didn't schedule things the way they had before and were always prepared to cancel at the last minute. "Her cancer recurred twice, and there was always a degree of uncertainty."

In fact, high-powered jobs might be the one remaining reason why some women choose to keep their cancer a secret. I was shocked when a woman I've known since university told me she'd had five surgeries, including a mastectomy and reconstruction, the spring before. We're not close friends, but I see her in passing almost weekly. I had no inkling. A top lawyer, she was worried that her clients would bolt if they knew she was ill. An academic I know tells more or less the same story.

I understand. I didn't have a "real" job when I was diagnosed, and I worried that writing a column about breast cancer would make me unemployable. I suspect there is some gender bias in this. I believe that men who are similarly successful and financially secure don't doubt their ability to come back after a recovery.

Many people tell me that I'm brave to write about my cancer experience. I never thought of it that way, though sometimes it did feel a bit like an out-of-body experience. Once I decided to do it, I was committed to telling the whole story. I found myself writing about things I would normally never talk about, pulling them out in much the same way I would if I were interviewing someone else.

People often ask me if writing about my cancer experience is cathartic. The answer is no. Writing has been very satisfying, but not because it gave me a chance to pour out my feelings. Writing and reporting are what I do for a living. Writing meant that I could work while I was going through the cancer experience, that I could feel I was doing something useful. That was a blessing because my anxiety over cancer and work was very real, even though I realized I was overreacting. I had been in discussions about a new job when I was diagnosed, but nothing was firm. That worried me, even though I would be working for my brother. At the time it seemed realistic. In fact, I started the new job during the "good week" between my second and third chemo treatments.

I start a new job today—developing, producing, and hosting a regular feature aimed at baby boomers for Classical 96.3 FM in Toronto. I'm working part-time to start, and that's certainly not the ideal way to go into a new situation. But going to the office, meeting my new colleagues, and tackling a new challenge is easing my second anxiety, after my health: What will cancer do to my career?

I WAS IN A better position than many cancer patients. The list of media people whose careers have bounced back after cancer is long. Pamela Wallin was appointed consul general in New York after a bout of colon cancer. Beverly Thomson hosted CTV's *Canada AM* after her treatment for breast cancer. The CBC's Wendy Mesley worked when she was able to during chemo for breast cancer, then returned to work full-time.

My own comeback was inauspicious. On my third day back, a friend picked me up for lunch, but we never made it to the restaurant. We had a car accident on the way. We were hit on the driver's side, the windshield blew out, and the car was badly damaged. My friend had a few cracked ribs. A piece of glass nicked my eye, and I hit my head on the roof and strained my neck. We were very lucky.

Needless to say, I never got back to work that day. Instead I went to see a doctor. A few days later, Dr. Warner asked me why my eye was red. I told her about the accident. "It's an interesting existential question," she concluded. "You spend all your energy treating and worrying about how cancer will affect your life, but something like a car accident can get you at any time."

13

The Other C-Word

I am celebrating my nephew Leith's bar mitzvah in Vancouver. In the lead-up to the event, I joked that it felt like my bar—or rather, bat—mitzvah. I'd been asked to chant a portion of the Torah during the service. I accepted the honour without realizing how much work was involved. Like Leith, I also needed bar mitzvah lessons. Learning to chant the Hebrew text was surprisingly satisfying. It's not that I am becoming more religious. But this ceremony feels like a rite of passage for me too. The beginning of my life after. My life after breast cancer.

I WAS JUMPING the gun a little. I still had one cancer-related procedure left. The BRCA-2 genetic mutation I carry puts me at very high risk of developing ovarian cancer. The best way to protect myself was to remove my ovaries and tubes. I was overdue for the surgery. So I had decided I would have the procedure as soon as my major breast cancer treatment was over.

As the time drew near, however, I thought about postponing it. It didn't fit into my life. I simply didn't have time for another recovery. I was working three days a week and had promised to go full-time by May. That was the month the manuscript for this book was due to reach the publisher. Leaving the surgery for another year would have been more convenient. But my surgeon, Dr. Joan Murphy, who is head of the Division of Gynecologic Oncology at Princess Margaret Hospital in Toronto and an expert in ovarian cancer, didn't like that idea. She said I could wait until the summer, but she'd want another round of blood tests checking for cancer if I did.

I decided to go ahead with the surgery as originally planned, not because I was worried about ovarian cancer, but because I was tired of recovering from one treatment and feeling fabulous, only to undergo another one. I wanted it over. So I told Dr. Murphy that I was good to go any time after Leith's bar mitzvah (which was on St. Patrick's Day), and the surgery was scheduled for ten days later. It felt like the end of a long haul. I regarded it as a kind of annoyance. My feelings now were different from my feelings the previous summer, before my lumpectomy, when I couldn't wait to go under the knife, to get the cancer out of me.

This surgery was prophylactic. The actual treatment part was over. I had finished radiation a month before. The redness and irritation were almost entirely gone. My chemotherapy had ended the previous November. My hair was long and thick enough to look like a funky style that I chose, instead of a cancer patient's baby-soft, boxy regrowth. People had stopped asking me continually how I was, or telling me that I looked good. It was obvious that I was fine.

My doctors had warned me that many patients find this the most difficult time. When the non-stop doctors' appointments taper off, they lose the reassurance of constant monitoring, and feel adrift, unsure, and afraid. They feel pressured to pick up where they left off, to return to normal life, but living with cancer is anything but normal. My friends tell me they achieve a "new normal." The problem is that family, friends, and colleagues don't realize that's what it is. They think it's over, but it isn't.

I hadn't experienced the anxiety of doctorless days. At least not yet. Of course, I hadn't gone longer than five days without a medical appointment. Frankly I was looking forward to it. But I felt like I was in a strange kind of limbo. My cancer was neither in the present nor the past.

"Libby had breast cancer last year," was how my friend Larissa explained it when she reintroduced me to someone I had met before breast cancer. I suppressed my annoyance. I remember thinking, What does she mean, last year? "Actually I just finished radiation three weeks ago," I corrected her. She rephrased it, "I meant that you had chemo last year." By then I was thinking, What does she mean, "had" breast cancer?

————————————

It certainly doesn't feel like it's over, and I'm not sure how I will know when it is. As far as my doctors know, the first surgery removed all the cancer from my body and my chances of avoiding a recurrence are excellent. True, I have a much higher than average chance of getting cancer again because I have the gene. But I'm taking steps to prevent that. That's why I'm having the surgery. That's why I'm taking tamoxifen to suppress estrogen. That's why I will have more screening and follow-up than other women. That is my new normal. So maybe it is just a matter of marking time— passing three years, five years, ten years, cancer-free.

I WAS PONDERING all of this as I sat in Larissa's kitchen in Vancouver, realizing that she thought my brush with cancer was over, even if I didn't. Larissa herself had just been diagnosed with breast cancer, and I understood that talking about my disease in the past tense helped her feel that there would come a day when her cancer was behind her.

But how did I feel about it? I decided I'd let my doctors mark the end point, though I didn't expect them to tell me anything I didn't already know. I had appointments with both my radiation oncologist and my medical oncologist coming up as soon as I returned to Toronto. I intended to question them closely, as much for this book as for my own information as a patient. What I heard from my radiation oncologist was a shock, but I was so busy taking notes and being a professional reporter that it took days to sink in.

"I consider you cured," says my radiation oncologist. Dr. Pignol tells me that he calls a cure based on the numbers: "When there is at least a 90 per cent chance that the cancer won't come back. Your chances are probably even better." He concedes that using the other C-word is a personal choice. "Sure, there's a small chance it can come back, but nothing is zero risk in life," he says.

DR. PIGNOL SEEMED animated by something almost like religious zeal as he explained how he comes to tell some of his patients they are cured. "What is the impact if I say you're not cured, you're in remission? It impacts the quality of life, and it's not helpful," he said. He reports that many patients who hear this become frightened every time they get a flu, a cough, or any small medical problem.

His decision to use the word *cure* is also cultural. Dr. Pignol is French. He practised in both the Alsace region and Nice, as well as in Paris. In Alsace, where the people are Germanic in origin, his patients were generally stoic about the first C-word, cancer, and recurrence. In Nice, where he characterizes the population as more Latin in temperament, it was the opposite. There he saw how debilitating the fear of recurrence could be.

Dr. Pignol recounted the words of one of his patients, who told him about the "nightmare" of her follow-ups. "I start being very nervous a week before because I have to go back to the hospital. Then I do my mammogram, and I have no clue what it shows, so I freak out," she told him. "I don't sleep at night because I don't know what's going on, and I start fighting with my husband." She explained that when she went to the doctor to hear her results, she'd arrive early and spend hours worrying in the waiting room, only to have the doctor spend five minutes with her to say, "You're fine; see you in six months." She cried all night after every appointment. "I had an early stage breast cancer, and I know I'm cured. Somebody should just tell me I'm cured."

"So I told her, 'You are.' " Dr. Pignol remembers thinking that the medical profession was imposing a heavy burden on this patient instead of helping her. He realized that living with the maybe attached to the word remission was destructive.

The very definition of the word *remission* is slippery. According to the *Oxford English Dictionary*, it is "a temporary lessening of the severity of disease or pain." The medical website www.medicinenet.com defines it as "disappearance of the signs and symptoms of cancer or other disease." That's the part both sources agree on. But unlike the dictionary, the website says "a remission can be temporary or permanent."

Dr. Pignol has a statistical threshold for using the word *cure*. "When a patient has a 90 per cent chance of surviving, I'm not going to scare her for five years, and that's where medicine is an art. In medicine it's always a guess," he said, "whether you say someone is cured or they are not." As for me, he really likes my odds. "In my opinion, you are cured."

"With cancer, you can't use the word *cure*," says my medical oncologist. I ask her if there will ever come a time when she tells me I'm cured. "When you die at ninety-five, and an autopsy shows that you are free of cancer," Dr. Warner replies.

DR. WARNER WON'T use the other C-word, at least not without a qualifier. She adheres to the traditional view of cancer in western medicine: it's unlike other diseases because even if it hasn't recurred after a set number of years, it still can. She will go as far as speaking of a "potential cure," in patients whose disease hasn't recurred for years. Dr. Pignol, my radiation oncologist, isn't such a stickler. "Yes, I have seen a recurrence after twenty years," he told me, "but I've seen it in one patient out of five thousand. That doesn't change my view."

Instead of saying I'm cured, Dr. Warner told me there's no evidence of cancer in my body. "Just assume it's not going to come back; it's pointless to assume anything else."

Nor does she like the word *remission*. "I use it only when I know the cancer is going to come back, but it is just sitting there for the moment."

When does she know for sure it's going to come back? "When a patient has Stage 4 metastatic breast cancer, we know it's incurable," she explains. "If we give that patient chemotherapy, the cancerous masses can disappear, and we'd call that a complete clinical remission, but we know that sooner or later the disease is going to come back."

"You can never be sure it's going to come back," said Dr. Pignol, "and you can't be sure it will never come back. You can find literature on women who were metastatic and who survived a long time."

For Dr. Warner that would be the exception that proves the rule, the special case when "a remission that normally lasts two years would last ten or twenty years."

Dr. Warner's certainty extends only to patients with Stage 4 disease. She said women with Stage 1, Stage 2, even Stage 3 cancer, can experience that "potential cure."

Dr. Pignol, meanwhile, will use the word *cure* only with early stage patients. The good news is, that accounts for most breast cancer patients these days.

There are many reasons other doctors don't like the word *cure*. If the worst does happen after a patient has been told she's cured, it's much harder for the patient to come to terms with a recurrence. Doctors also worry that hearing the other C-word could make some patients over-confident, foregoing the follow-up and screening they will need year in, year out. Of course, the constant round of tests, imaging, and check-ups makes it harder for patients to put cancer behind them.

I saw Dr. Pignol and Dr. Warner back to back. Intellectually, I understood that they agreed on my prognosis, that they were both basically telling me the same thing, that theirs was a semantic disagreement. Maybe we need a new word—a word that recognizes that cancer can be a highly treatable chronic disease, a word that means "as good as cured."

But there is no denying the power of the other C-word, delivered without a qualifier. Cured. I experienced it as what the French call a *coup de foudre*—the big bang or explosion usually associated metaphorically with love at first sight. It's the difference between hearing that someone loves you or just likes you a lot.

At first, I felt unsettled. As I left the hospital, I realized I was distracted—dangerously distracted as it turned out—but I didn't realize why. It took me nearly half an hour to find my car—in a lot I had parked in thirty or forty times!

My husband was away, and I prepared dinner for myself at home later. First, I thought my electric grill was broken. The plug is a bit finicky, and I fiddled with it for a long time before I realized I hadn't turned the thing on. Then I became impatient for the fish to cook because I was so hungry. But I forced myself to sit down and wait instead of poking at it every few seconds. I was sitting with my back turned when I realized the grill was on fire, just minutes away from setting the kitchen alight!

Usually I experience this kind of distracted agitation only with bad things. The near-fire made me try to understand why I was so discombobulated. I had just been given permission to let go of a thing—a very bad thing, the C-word, *cancer*—that had overtaken and defined my life for the last ten months. But the other C-word, *cure*, was taking me into new territory. It was like a line in the sand separating my life during cancer from my life after. Women who don't hear the other C-word don't experience that.

"With my doctor there was never a clear line of demarcation, no mention of cure or remission," wrote Elizabeth, a woman who had been treated for early stage breast cancer. This didn't surprise her. "I had done a lot of research beforehand, so I knew the language of cure/remission had been pretty much replaced with n.e.d. (no evidence of disease)." Elizabeth finished chemo and radiation and started on hormone therapy. "It was just the next phase," she said.

And hearing the word *cure* doesn't have the same effect on everyone. Bonnie, the woman who wrote me many times, starting soon after her diagnosis was told that her oncologist considered her cured. "Do I feel it's all over or behind me ... ABSOLUTELY NOT, NO ... I think it will always be part of me ... I think this time now is so much harder."

I wondered how long it took my mother to let it go. Growing up, I never had the sense that she worried about a relapse. So I didn't either. Maybe she was just very good at protecting me from her worst fears.

I don't have children, so I don't have to worry about how my disease would impact them. It's a huge issue for parents, and it's hard to tell if and when kids get over it. My friend Gill, who was successfully treated for leukemia three years ago, told me she never thinks about it any more. But recently, her eleven-year-old daughter asked her if there was still a chance she could die of the disease. It was a rude awakening. Gill thought her children had put it behind them.

Larissa worried about how her four kids would handle things. She and her husband have been very open with them, even taking them along to the chemo clinic. "Don't be upset if the kids are checking you out more than usual," she told me as we got out of the car to get coffee. "They know that Auntie Libby had breast cancer too, and I've told them to see for themselves how well you're doing now."

Which was unnecessary. Actually, I was hoping that my visit would reassure her entire family. When we got back into the car, I announced to the kids, "You can ask me anything you want about cancer, any time; it's okay." They didn't have any questions for me, and I can only guess at how they were processing my announcement. Still, they already had a lot more information than I had all those years ago, when I was their age and my mother was sick. Despite which, I managed to grow up carefree, at least when it came to cancer. So I don't know which way is better.

I've been channelling my mother a lot lately. I've dyed my hair auburn, close to the colour she had. At Leith's bar mitzvah service, I wore the same outfit she wore to Sam's (Leith's father's) bar mitzvah. Along with the matching pillbox hat.

As for the singing, it could have gone better. Despite hours of practice, I started out too high and didn't get back to a key I could carry until my portion was almost over. The good news is I may get a do-over. My niece Chaya, who is ten, isn't sure she wants a bat mitzvah. Her mother, Lesley, suggested that Chaya and I do it together—a double bat mitzvah. I never had one, so I'm game. The timing would be auspicious. Chaya will be ready in three years, and three years is the time frame in which cancer is most likely to come back. That would certainly make it an appropriate time for my rite of passage. It will be over when the lady in her mother's dress sings again.

14

The Good News About Cancer

The irony! I am listening to the first reports about the huge increase in survival rates for both breast and prostate cancer when I notice tributes to two people who have just died of these diseases. The first is a woman I met only once; the other is a colleague on a charitable board. The good news goes in one ear as I read the two obituaries and prepare to attend the colleague's funeral the next day.

THE DEATH RATE from breast cancer has dropped 25 per cent in the last twenty years. A full 86 per cent of women now survive at least five years after their diagnosis. This stunning accomplishment should comfort cancer patients and their families.

The good news comes from a piece of research produced by the Canadian Cancer Society, the National

Cancer Institute of Canada, Statistics Canada, the provincial/territorial cancer registries and the Public Health Agency of Canada. But for me, it is punctuated by those two death notices.

Gordy Wolfe was a passionate community activist who worked with people living in poverty, victims of violence, and youth. He gave countless hours to his synagogue, Holy Blossom Temple, where his funeral was standing-room only, and to other Jewish community groups, including the Ashkenaz Foundation, where he and I worked together. Gordy would have had many more years of productive volunteering had he not died of prostate cancer at the age of seventy.

Kristine Bogyo was an accomplished cellist and the conductor and founder of Toronto's Mooredale Youth Orchestra. I met her at a charitable concert given by her husband, renowned pianist Anton Kuerti. I did not know she had breast cancer, and she probably didn't know that I had it too. She was diagnosed at the age of forty-seven and lived with the disease for thirteen years. Kristine's mother had died of breast cancer at the age of fifty.

Is Kristine's story part of the good news or the bad news? I do not know the details of her case—the stage or type of breast cancer that she had. But her case would have been counted in those hopeful numbers. She was diagnosed within the last twenty years and survived more, many more, than five years. She lived ten years longer than her own mother did. But she was a vital, talented woman who died much too soon.

The biggest factor behind the improvement in survival is early detection. If you catch cancer before it spreads, your chances of beating it go up exponentially. And cancer treatment is better. "The treatment for every stage of cancer has improved a lot," said Dr. Warner. "People are less likely to relapse than they would have been ten or fifteen years ago, and if they have a recurrence, they do better."

One of those improved treatments has the promise of pointing the way to a cure for cancer. The drug Herceptin (generic name: trastuzumab) is a treatment for a particularly aggressive form of breast cancer called HER2/neu-positive. Caused by a mistake in the gene, but not hereditary, it happens when the cell replicates. No one knows why. This type of cancer hits two-hundred-and-fifty thousand women around the world every year, accounting for a quarter of all breast cancer cases. It spreads earlier than other types of breast cancer—sometimes when the tumour is minuscule; it recurs faster than other breast cancers; and the relapses tend to be more widespread. For patients, the survival is shorter. Or it was in the pre-Herceptin era.

Dr. Dennis Slamon of the UCLA School of Medicine headed up the team that discovered Herceptin in the early 1990s. I talked to him when he visited Toronto to pick up the 2007 Gairdner International Award for Medical Research. "I don't have the data yet, but I bet you we can improve the cure rates by about one-third with Herceptin," he told me after his lunch speech atop the Sutton Place Hotel.

Herceptin is what he calls a "targeted therapy." It attacks the genetic mutation that causes the disease. That's completely different from chemotherapy, which attacks the entire system in the hope that it will kill off cancer cells too. "The ultimate goal would be to get rid of chemo," said Dr. Slamon. "If we can identify what's broken, we won't throw in these non-specific bombs."

The success of Herceptin has made the hunt for other targeted therapies a popular area of research. Dr. Slamon said there are some promising developments—not just for breast cancer, but also for lung, colorectal, and prostate cancers.

"If I could, I'd go hug him," one woman said to me after Dr. Slamon's speech. She had two Herceptin treatments left and was very grateful, although it was too soon to tell whether the drug was working.

Dr. Slamon will consider her cured if she survives for six or seven years. *Cure* is not a word he uses lightly. "I think it sets expectations inappropriately," he said. "But if you identify what's broken, and you treat it effectively, it isn't just turning the cancer into a chronic disease. You should be able to eradicate the disease."

Kristine Bogyo lived ten years longer than her mother did. If I live ten years longer than my mother did, I would get to celebrate my eighty-third birthday. I would likely die of something else. And maybe I'd live to see a cure for cancer.

I never thought a story on breast cancer would make me laugh out loud. That's what happens as soon as I see the headline: "Housework wards off breast cancer." Actually, I wonder if it's a joke. Sarah, my editor at the *National Post*, sent it to me. It is three days before New Year's, and I suspect that Sarah is colluding with Doug. He's always trying to make me promise to be a better housekeeper, especially at this time of year.

IT TURNED OUT the story was for real, based on British research published in the journal *Cancer Epidemiology Biomarkers*. It wasn't about housework, exactly, rather the link between exercise and breast cancer. It showed that moderate forms of regular physical activity, such as housework, were more effective in preventing breast cancer than was more intense but less frequent exercise. Still, from London, England, to Melbourne, Australia, the headlines proclaimed that "Housework Cuts Cancer."

It's enough to make you burn your bra, but at least this one was funny. The fallout from another, earlier story was anything but. On December 18, 2006, newspapers around the country picked up on a story comparing three different chemotherapy regimens for breast cancer. The research had been presented at a major breast cancer conference in Texas. It concluded that one of the three cocktails—AC/T, a combination of the drugs Adriamycin (generic name: doxorubicin) and cyclophosphamide, followed by Taxol (generic name: paclitaxel)—was less effective at preventing a recurrence of breast cancer than were the other two drug combinations studied. Now imagine your reaction if you were a patient taking AC/T. It would be hard to put a lid on the anxiety even if you weren't.

My heart stopped when I saw the acronym AC/T, even though I took AC only and didn't get the additional paclitaxel. I remembered how relieved I was when Dr. Warner told me that four rounds of AC were all I needed. That memory didn't stop me from worrying when I saw this story. By the time I finished the second paragraph, however, I realized the new findings didn't apply to me. All the women studied had breast cancer that had spread to their lymph nodes. Mine hadn't. Still, my first instinct was to second-guess my treatment and start calling my doctors. It took some effort to suppress it.

"I didn't call either," my friend Christine told me. Christine fits the profile of the women in this study, and she had just been treated with the AC/T combination. In her place, I would have been in a tizzy, but Christine is fatalistic. "What would be the point? It's done," she said. "I'm not going to go back and do more chemo." Christine is a lawyer and very analytical. Chemotherapy prevents a recurrence of cancer in only a small percentage of cases. Christine figures that since it works in only 5 per cent of cases like hers, she's not going to get excited about something that may increase those numbers marginally. "I figure I'm either in the right percentage or not," she said.

Few patients have that discipline. My nurse oncologist, Anita, said fully 30 per cent of her patients called after that story appeared. Two of her oncologist friends reported the same thing: phones ringing off the hook with anxious patients worrying they got inferior treatment. "It's great to inform the public," she said, "but it doesn't help the people who are in the midst of going through this. Anybody on chemo stops and says, "Could it be me?""

Dr. Warner braces herself when she sees stories like this. "I read and go, oh my God, I can think of twenty women who are going to be very upset, thinking they went through all that and didn't get the best treatment," she said. "The way some women see it, they got the wrong treatment, and they're going to die."

Anita said it's even worse when people don't read articles but just hear about them. Every cancer patient gets second-, third-, and even fourth-hand reports of the latest discoveries, and these, too, can lead to a lot of anxiety. "That's the thing I really hate about these articles," she said, "they lead to broken telephone syndrome."

The first thing to remember is that any research is carried out on people who share certain characteristics. The results apply only to people with those characteristics. I had the right idea when I forced myself to stop fretting after realizing the new findings didn't relate to me.

But it isn't easy to do that, and well-meaning family and friends can make it harder. I can't count the number of emails and clippings I've received about advances in cancers that are completely different from mine. I dismiss these reports firmly, but they always put me on edge.

The Canadian Cancer Society cautions patients to be skeptical, even if new information does apply to them. Every new study provides a small piece of the puzzle. Doctors change the way they practise only if there's a whole new body of evidence on a given subject. "It's rare that a single study is strong enough to affect the way patients are treated," said Dr. Barbara Whylie, CEO of the Canadian Cancer Society. "Talk to your oncologist. That's the person who understands your situation."

Dr. Warner, however, may qualify that advice. "People read the first two paragraphs of a story, and I have to go into damage control," she said. There are three kinds of stories she hates, starting with the ones about diet. She reminded me about an article that reported that women who eat more red meat are at higher risk of getting breast cancer. I remembered reading it while I was doing chemo. I was eating a lot of meat at the time because the drugs ruined my taste for fish. It was bad enough to be put off my regular diet. I didn't need the added worry that it might hurt my prognosis. Fortunately, I read further and saw that many of the women in the group that had eaten more meat were also obese and sedentary. That wasn't the only caveat.

"There are also red meat studies that show it has no effect," said Dr. Warner. "Diet stories drive people crazy because no matter what you eat, there's a problem: mercury in fish or whatever..." she said, "and it changes from month to month."

The second kind she hates are certain kinds of drug stories. "Sometimes the media will pick up a story about a drug that's been around for ten years but is now being marketed differently, and they turn it into a big drug breakthrough," she explains. As a member of the media, I take her point. We don't always know enough to cut through the pharmaceutical industry spin. Our readers should watch for it too.

But the third kind, the ones she hates the most, are stories from the lab—stories about preliminary animal studies that show promise for humans. "The next thing you know, six of your patients walk in with the article, and they want the experimental compound now," she said. "So I tell them it's the best time ever to be a rat with breast cancer."

If you're sick, however, and there's a breakthrough or an advance, it's natural to wonder, Why can't I have that treatment now? It might save my life. Eminent Canadian cancer researcher Dr. Tak Mak said patients must be patient when they read about what's happening in the laboratory today. "If a miracle occurs, it'll help patients ten years from now," he said. "If there's no miracle, it'll take fifteen or twenty years."

Back in 1984, Dr. Mak was the first to isolate and clone the genes for the human T-cell receptor. T-cell receptors allow the body to identify abnormal cells and target them for destruction. Since Dr. Mak's landmark discovery, other scientists have built on his work. There have been thirty thousand papers on the subject, and his original paper has been cited twelve hundred times. But he cautions, "It has very little to do with breast cancer today; it is something for the future." He describes the T-cell receptor as a conceptual and scientific tool. "Will it become the Holy Grail of immunology?" he asks. "We'll have to wait and see."

Cancer patients don't have time to wait and see. Dr. Mak knows this well. He lost his wife, Shirley, to breast cancer in 1997. At the time, he said, "My torment was that I knew all about this disease. I knew how it worked, but I couldn't do anything against it. I was helpless."

To me, this seems like an epic tragedy—the gods punishing hubris. Dr. Mak is not arrogant. On the contrary, he seems remarkably modest, given his accomplishments. But a Greek god would undoubtedly consider the drive to conquer cancer hubris.

Meanwhile, watching a loved one die can be even worse when there is so much good news, and when so many others are surviving the same disease.

15

The Final Surgery

"I'm having surgery for prostate cancer," says Allan, almost cheer-fully. I haven't seen him for years. This in the last place I'd expect to run into an old friend—the surgical waiting room at Toronto General Hospital, at six o'clock in the morning. I admire his atti-tude. I remember the anxious hours I spent in the waiting room before my first cancer surgery, nine months ago. I would never have been able to carry on a conversation like this. I've come a long way since then. All my tough decisions are behind me. I am here today for surgery of a different kind.

THE SURGERY TO have my ovaries and tubes removed was the last part of my treatment. It is standard practice for women who have the gene muta-tion that I have. But many patients who don't also opt to have the surgery. This procedure can help prevent a recurrence in a woman whose breast cancer feeds off estrogen because it removes any residual estrogen from the body. It also makes it possible for a woman to take a class of hormone therapy drugs called aromatase inhibitors. To be eligible for these drugs, a woman who has not been in full menopause for at least a year has to have her ovaries removed.

My gynecologic oncologist at Princess Margaret Hospital, Dr. Murphy, had wanted me to have a full hysterectomy, and I originally agreed. I had watched my mother die of ovarian cancer, and that disease scared me a lot more than breast cancer. When I first tested positive for the BRCA-2 mutation, my genetic counsellors insisted that the surgery was not optional, and I took them at their word. By the time I saw Dr. Murphy six months later, I was resigned to it.

"I understand we have a done deal," she said at our first pre-operative meeting. She seemed a little surprised, and relieved, that she didn't have to launch into a surgical sales job. I knew my ovaries and tubes had to go, but I'd heard conflicting reports about the rest of my reproductive apparatus. The one thing I knew for sure was that I wanted laparoscopic surgery.

"You may as well let them take your uterus too if they can do it laparoscopically," advised one friend, a physician who has also had breast cancer. I understood the rationale: tamoxifen, the hormone therapy drug I would be on for five years, increases the risk of uterine cancer. Removing my uterus would eliminate that risk.

"Don't touch your uterus," advised another friend, who also has the BRCA-2 gene mutation. "It increases the risk of nicking your bowel during surgery, and that would be awful."

Dr. Murphy assured me she wouldn't puncture my bowel, and I signed the papers. She was cautiously optimistic about doing the procedure laparoscopically. The only possible problem was scar tissue from previous operations, so there was a chance she would encounter obstacles when I was on the table. I had to sign a second consent form for a laparotomy—full, open surgery—in case that happened. If she had to open me up, my recovery would be six weeks instead of two, and much more difficult. I had been working very hard on my "core" with my new trainer, Tami, and the idea of cutting through my abdominal muscles upset me. But I also knew that having this at the top of my list of concerns was a sign of how well I was doing.

If the laparoscopy was a go, Dr. Murphy would make three tiny incisions in my abdomen—one on the right where I had a scar from an appendectomy, one just inside my belly button, and one above my pubic bone—and insert a scope to perform the procedure. I'd already had laparoscopic knee surgery, so I thought I had all the information.

My friend Linda set me straight. She had recently had laparoscopic surgery for colon cancer, and we were having dinner together about three weeks after her operation and three days before mine. "You know they inject you with gas during the procedure, don't you?" she asked. No one said anything to me about gas, I told her. "Well they do, and you should be prepared because you'll feel uncomfortable and you'll be burping for days after."

My friend Elsa supplied even more details. Elsa loves to watch reality surgery shows on television. It helps her unwind from a hard day in the trenches of the accessories business. She couldn't believe my ignorance. "They don't just inject some gas," she said. "They blow you up like a balloon; your stomach will be huge when you're on the table."

One way or another, my hard-earned, nearly flat stomach was going to come out softer and bigger after the surgery. But by then I was worrying about something more primal. "Sex Question," in bold letters, read the subject line of the email I sent Dr. Murphy the day after our meeting. I wanted to know if a hysterectomy could impair my sex life. "The surgery will do little if anything to the current state of your 'drive,'" she wrote back. "And anatomically, there is little likelihood it will cause any significant change in sexual function. If things are working well now, the surgery is unlikely to upset those things." So that was that, until I talked to Anita. "Make sure that removing your cervix won't cause bladder problems," she cautioned. My cervix? At that point I couldn't remember if I'd agreed to have that removed as well.

Dr. Murphy explained that with the procedure she uses, the cervix has to come out along with the uterus. She said that bladder problems are usually the result of pregnancy, not the surgery itself. "But I have to tell you, some women report sexual feeling in the area of the cervix," she said. Now I was really confused. "Remind me where it is exactly?" I asked sheepishly.

There was one worry I didn't have. In normal circumstances, this surgery will bring on menopause. For me, the chemotherapy had already put me into menopause. (After chemotherapy I had had a lot of hot flashes, maybe as many as forty a day, but they weren't bad. After this surgery my hot flashes virtually stopped.)

Dr. Murphy understood that all my questions amounted to strong second thoughts about the operation. Her solution: downsize the surgery. She said that since I showed no evidence of disease, a smaller operation was a reasonable alternative. She told me that while she preferred a full hysterectomy as a preventive measure, other cancer centres did not recommend that. "I feel totally comfortable just taking your ovaries and tubes."

I instantly knew it was the right thing. I realized I felt much better about accepting a small increase in the risk of some future cancer rather than taking any chance of having bowel, bladder, or sexual problems in the present.

Dr. Warner had summed it up perfectly a few weeks before. "I think for you, the hardest part of this has been making all these decisions," she said. It was true. Agonizing over the surgical options for preventing another cancer was much worse than undergoing chemo or radiation, or the anxiety of knowing I had cancer. This was the last of those decisions.

The first thing I noticed when I woke up were the downtown buildings I could see through the window. They seemed to beckon me to return to the workaday world. I swear I could hear a din from that direction. I knew the laparoscopy had been successful. Someone must have told me in the recovery room, but I didn't remember.

It was so different from the time I woke up after my lumpectomy. That is one memory I will never forget—Dr. Arnaout hovering over me, telling me the cancer had not spread to my lymph nodes. I can still feel the relief and gratitude wash over me. That was the defining moment of this journey. That was the instant I began to see my treatment, however difficult, as a temporary annoyance I would bear as cheerfully as possible.

This time I didn't even remember being in the recovery room. I woke up on the ward feeling hungry, asking Doug for coffee and food, against doctor's orders. When the nurse came to help me to the washroom, I sat up with no pain or problem. "Now that I'm up, we may as well go for a walk," I told her. The nurse gave me that "you are an amazing patient" look. I loved it. It made me feel like a kid who got a gold star. I started walking faster than she was. I was in a hurry to leave the hospital.

16

Cosmetics

I'm very lucky. My husband and I are closer because of the cancer. I may not like the way my breast looks, but it hasn't stopped me from intimacy, sex, or having a good time.

FOR WOMEN WITH breast cancer, the issue of body image and sexuality is the elephant in the room. It's the only subject I've been reticent about. Women don't usually bring it up on their own, and doctors don't ask. Friends may discuss it, but I'm not convinced they necessarily tell the truth. I know I don't.

"Women feel they should just be so damn glad to be alive, they're inhibited about talking about the more subtle areas," said Dr. Mary Jane Esplen, who is leading a study on body image, quality of life, and relationships after breast cancer for three major hospitals in Toronto. "They are afraid people will perceive them as vain and trivial."

Dr. Esplen said 20 per cent to 40 per cent of women have serious problems that can last long after their treatment ends. Some don't want to be held or touched, let alone have sex. Some can't look at themselves, let alone allow their partners to look. Dr. Esplen runs a support group and leads imaging exercises that involve looking in the mirror. "I've had women who say, 'I don't even think that's my body.' One woman told me she couldn't see her torso. The only part of her reflection that registered was her head, and from her thighs on down."

Dr. Esplen had assumed that women who'd had lumpectomies would fare better emotionally than those who'd had mastectomies, but that's not necessarily true. She said in many cases they are equally distressed. "We have women with lumpectomies who really struggle with negative self-image around the shape of their breasts and the loss of sensations. They feel unequal, and they're upset that their two breasts are different."

That's what upsets me. After surgery, my left breast is smaller, rounder, and perkier than the right. I am thankful for one thing: it doesn't show in clothes. When I found the lump, it was quite high on my chest, and I assumed that after surgery, I wouldn't be able to wear anything lower than a crewneck. The scar is about two inches beneath that, so I can wear tight clothes or show cleavage without looking different from before. But when I take my clothes off, I don't like what I see.

Three of my friends with mastectomies feel better about what they confront in the mirror. Madeline wasn't a candidate for breast reconstruction because she had to have radiation after her surgery. She doesn't care. When she looks at herself, the missing breast almost doesn't register. "I look in the mirror and think, I have a beautiful body," she said. Madeline calls her prosthesis the "chicken thing." I've seen her whip it out playfully in public. "She seems to compensate by wearing her skirts shorter and shorter," her colleague John told me when we were all at a summer conference together, less than a month after my surgery. Then the conversation turned to me.

"How are you?" he asked, staring at my breasts, addressing them, actually. "You had a ... a lum—?"

"A lumpectomy," I interrupted. He didn't take his eyes off my boobs. I realized, with some satisfaction, that men would continue to look at my breasts after cancer, even if they looked a little confused.

That's part of the reason I don't like to talk about what my breasts look like. They can "pass" for looking nice, so I think I should just keep my mouth shut and pretend they are.

That means dressing and carrying myself exactly as I used to, and that itself has a positive effect. Doing this for a while made me wonder if I was wrong, if for all my whining I actually had better results than most women. So I asked my medical oncologist. She explained that on some women, usually those with big breasts and small cancers, you can hardly tell. "Your cosmetic results are average,"

Dr. Warner told me. I felt like a straight-A student who had just received her first C. Up until that moment, I'd been an above-average cancer patient. I was like an over-achieving high-school kid desperate to be the best in the class. And I'd been lucky. I "sailed" through my treatment—that was the way Dr. Warner put it—maintaining my work life, my social life, and my exercise regimen. Now I felt I was falling short.

My friend Barb has a better attitude, even though she's had a mastectomy. Fortunately, she doesn't mind if people know. Barb bothers to wear a prosthesis only to work or for an evening out. "My breasts were small to begin with," she said, "so if I just wear a sports bra, it's hard to tell." Barb decided against having a reconstruction. "I just didn't want to go through any more recovery," she told me. I understand that. I feel the same way. With my treatment over, the idea of putting myself through unnecessary surgery seems awful. But I am planning to do it. I want to have plastic surgery to "rebalance" my breasts as soon as I can.

My friend Anne can't understand this. Anne is in her sixties, and she's a powerhouse. She lost a breast to cancer about twenty years ago and decided to have the other one removed prophylactically when she discovered, years later, that she had the BRCA-2 mutation. She's happier with both off. She never even considered a reconstruction. "It doesn't interfere with my romantic life," she told me, "and I have no qualms about walking around naked at the gym."

I developed a whole new routine for changing at the gym. My locker is in the most open part of the room. I used to be completely uninhibited about taking my clothes off. Now I put a towel over my bra, find an inner row that's empty, then pull off my bra, leaving myself covered with the towel. But I'm improving. I've started to change quickly in my own spot if no one is around, and I don't freak out if anyone happens to walk by before I'm finished.

At least my new modesty didn't stop me from going to the gym. Dr. Esplen told me about one of her patients, who cancelled her annual European trip to visit family by the sea because she couldn't face changing to go to the beach. "I'm not ready, there's no way I'm going to be in a change room or in a bathing suit," she told her support group. This woman is petite and beautiful, according to Dr. Esplen, and looks like a young Jane Seymour. She had a lumpectomy and isn't happy with the shape of her breast. "The wrong thing to say is, What are you talking about? You're beautiful, and there are so many bathing suit styles," said Dr. Esplen. The right thing is to help her express her anger. "She's thinking she will never look like she used to, and that for the rest of her life, every time she dates someone new she'll have to tell him she had breast cancer and show it to him." Dr. Esplen said it is a matter of mourning a loss. "There has to be some grieving, and a lot of stuff has to happen around the confrontation and the loss."

The other thing that happens to women with breast cancer is weight gain, or loss, something they usually don't anticipate. I didn't. Actually I assumed I'd lose my appetite and the pounds would melt away. In my mind, this was to be the silver lining of chemotherapy. I remember how shocked I was when Dr. Warner told me that women with breast cancer are more likely to gain weight than lose it.

I kept weight off by maintaining my exercise regimen. But not everyone is able to do that. Women gain weight because the drugs slow their metabolism or because they're nauseous and can eat only certain things. Sometimes they eat more because of the stress and because they're off their routine. Whatever the reason, it's hardly a shock that the weight gain can play havoc with body image.

A reader named Catherine wrote: "The most off-pissing part of it all was that I gained 25 pounds during chemo that I am still trying to lose [five years later]. The combo of steroids to help you tolerate chemo, the immediate onset of menopause, the post-chemo drugs that inhibit weight loss, etc., is not a good recipe for staying slim." Catherine has worked her way through it, though. "The cliché that cancer changes your life is of course a cliché for a reason. I've often said that if I didn't give too much of a crap what others thought before I had cancer, I give even less of a crap now—which is probably not good, but is great fun nonetheless."

Dr. Esplen suspects that the women who are most preoccupied with weight may have the toughest time adjusting. "Is there something about control, or the level of perfectionism, or how the body itself contributed to their self-esteem prior to the breast cancer?" she wonders.

It can take years to come to terms with these things and, in the meantime, that can ruin sex and intimacy. Dr. Esplen said many women are unhappy with their sex lives five and ten years later. It would be wrong to blame this strictly on breast cancer—there are other factors, such as menopause and aging—but the breast cancer is often the catalyst. These women have trouble being intimate with their partners. Sometimes they feel angry with their spouses, according to Dr. Esplen, often because they feel displaced from their own bodies. "It doesn't necessarily work if a husband tells his wife he finds her beautiful. Many women will wonder if that's what he really thinks," said Dr. Esplen, pointing out that women with eating disorders have similar reactions.

As for men, they often feel helpless. Many men feel their partners have become more fragile, and they are afraid of hurting them during sex. "It's new territory, their couplehood is altered," Dr. Esplen said. "But most men can handle the changed appearance. Most will say, 'I'm just so glad she's here.'"

But some men do leave. Stephanie wrote that she had two lumpectomies, and lost the front of her breast and nipple. Her boyfriend disappeared during the treatment. Meanwhile, she faced a wait of up to two years just for a consultation on breast reconstruction. Stephanie lives in Toronto and will probably travel to another city to have her operation sooner. "I feel crap enough about my half-breast body," she wrote. "I'm not a pessimistic person, but I would have liked some more warning about the physical loss I would be left with."

For Robyn, breast cancer was her second bout with the disease. "My first experience with cancer meant the end of my relationship with my spouse," she wrote. "He couldn't look at me without seeing cancer. It forced him to consider both my and his own mortality, something which he was so frightened of that he couldn't deal with it."

Robyn is philosophical. She came to realize that the relationship hadn't been fulfilling, that this wasn't a loss but a step to a happier life. Other women come to the same conclusion and initiate the breakup. "There's a growth that happens for some women, and they outgrow their partnership," said Dr. Esplen. "The man has come through something with her, but it really was her traumatic experience." She said couple therapy may help, but sometimes the relationship just doesn't work anymore. "They realize life may be short and think, I'm out of here."

I have a very practical attitude. I will have it fixed. If it still bugs me in a year, I'll have surgery on the other breast, reducing, reshaping, and lifting it so it matches the one that had the cancer. My husband doesn't want me to do it. He likes me the way I am. He doesn't really understand why this is something I'd do for myself, when he's the only person who sees me naked outside the locker room.

DR. ESPLEN SAID the best thing that can happen to a woman's self-image after cancer is a new sense of inner beauty and strength. There can be a freedom in coming through something like this. Some women, like Catherine, stop trying so hard to please others and enjoy life more. "They discover a new dimension, how much they could deal with," she said. "And they like that about themselves."

I feel I've achieved that new dimension, and that the changes in my outward appearance mirror what has happened inside. I've gone from a conventional-looking television reporter with a blonde bob to a hip woman with spiky auburn hair. That says it all. But I still don't like the way my breast looks.

17

Leaving Cancerland

Maybe it's the drugs. But as I get into the car that will drive me away from the hospital, I swear I see another sign beside the exit, the kind of sign you'd find at the limits of a picturesque town: "You are now leaving Cancerland."

YES, I WAS FEELING the pull of the world beyond cancer. Yes, I felt I had permission to put the disease behind me now that my radiation oncologist, Dr. Pignol, had said the word cure. But it was more than that. I also felt obliged. Obliged to leave Cancerland.

I'd had a meeting with Dr. Pignol, my radiation oncologist, and then one immediately after with Dr. Warner, my medical oncologist, a week before the surgery to remove my ovaries. I hadn't planned it that way. I'd actually missed an appointment with Dr. Warner in February, three

191

months after the end of chemo. I was in the middle of radiation at that point, in the hospital every day, and I just forgot. I rescheduled it for the same day as the appointment with Dr. Pignol for convenience. Seeing them one after the other made me feel like I was hogging the healthcare system. I didn't think it was medically necessary to see them both. These were my first follow-up visits, but I thought of them as formal end-of-treatment appointments, almost like exit interviews. With Dr. Pignol's, that's exactly what it turned out to be.

"I think Dr. Warner should follow you from now on," he said. "After all, she is the one with expertise in genetic breast cancer." I agreed there was no need for me to keep seeing them both. But Dr. Pignol was apologetic. "I want you to know that I'm here if you ever need me for anything," he said. He went on a bit, as if he wanted to make sure I didn't think he was abandoning me. Actually, I thought continuing with both doctors would be a waste of their time—and mine.

Bonnie reacted differently, even though her experience was virtually parallel to mine—early stage breast cancer, treated with surgery, chemo, radiation, and tamoxifen. She also had one doctor who told her she was cured and one who didn't like to use that word. But the end of treatment made her feel adrift: "The continuing uncertainties are more stressful because I am so much less involved with doctors. Instead of this having a positive effect, it seems to be doing the opposite," she wrote. "I feel like it's up to me to come up with the right plan to keep me cancer-free. I have gone from being at the centre of a very structured environment to a feeling of being free-floating. There is no road map to being cancer-free. The concept of being told you're cured is a relief emotionally, but intellectually completely misleading."

Is the problem that Bonnie doesn't believe her doctor? Or is it a question of how much uncertainty she can live with? When there is a small risk, 10 per cent or so, that the cancer will recur, it probably comes down to the way a person is wired. "I tell patients to live life as though they are cured," said Dr. Warner. "It's easier for some than for others."

It is especially difficult when the prognosis is tougher. After being cancer-free for four years, my friend Barb started waking up terrified in the middle of the night. She was having acute anxiety about a recurrence, even though there's no indication that this will happen.

Barb had Stage 3B breast cancer that spread to most of her lymph nodes (some medical institutions distinguish between 3 and 3B, which is more advanced; others don't). She researched her disease meticulously and asked a lot of tough questions. At the outset, her doctors told her she would not be cured. "We would hope to buy you five years, or in a very good scenario, ten," they said. "I asked what my odds were, and they told me," said Barb. "I can't blame them." Intellectually, Barb knows that the longer she's clear of cancer, the better her chances are. She knows her odds are brighter now, because she's on a new drug that wasn't available when she was first diagnosed. But that doesn't change the way she feels.

"If you asked me a year ago, I would have been more positive," said Barb. That's because cancer is most likely to recur within two or three years, and Barb had passed that critical milestone cancer-free. "But since I was told that I could buy five years, I think I'm getting to the end of my five-year term."

I asked my own doctors about this, and they thought Barb took a positive message and twisted it. Their take is that five- and ten-year survival rates are simply the numbers that oncologists deal with. But the longer a patient survives, the longer they are likely to. "It's normal for people to take what doctors say and spin it in some neurotic way," said Dr. Warner, "especially if they had a mother, a sister, or a friend who relapsed."

Sure enough, Barb said that she "started to feel whacked because of other people's news." She told me a terrible story about her friend's seemingly incomprehensible recurrence. Barb's friend had originally been diagnosed with DCIS (Ductal Carcinoma in Situ). It's called Stage 0. Some doctors don't consider it to be cancer, and the cure rate is close to 100 per cent. Five-and-a-half years later, this woman had a relapse that had spread to her bones and her lungs. "For me there is no rhyme or reason to who gets cancer back," said Barb. "It's never over, even if you think you're clear."

Sometimes it's hard to say which came first—the story about a recurrence or the fear of one. "Recently I've heard about many more of these cases," wrote Stephanie. "It's either because I'm looking for it or because I'm ready to hear it." Stephanie is also a patient of radiation oncologist Dr. Pignol, and he told her she was cured. "My boss's sister-in-law had breast cancer last year, was 'cured,' and now has Stage 4 liver cancer," she told me. "I met a woman at a party last week who was going in for a double mastectomy because she had a new and larger cancer after being 'cured' three years ago." And so the stories go. They don't have to involve someone close—or even someone you know. They are told and re-told by one cancer patient to another. Likely they lose accuracy and get worse along the way.

It can be worse when it happens to a person in the public eye. When Elizabeth Edwards announced that her breast cancer had recurred, the headlines focused on the couple's decision to continue John Edwards' campaign for presidential candidate. But for tens of thousands of women who'd been through breast cancer, that wasn't the story. The case of Elizabeth Edwards brought them face to face with the fear of a relapse. There it was, played out on television and in the newspapers. It had happened to someone powerful, someone who had every advantage. When Bonnie wrote me about her feeling that talk of being cured was "intellectually misleading," she confessed that she was upset because of Elizabeth Edwards. Stephanie also said that Edwards was a big part of her sense that she was surrounded by cases of relapse.

Which is ironic, because Edwards herself decided to live her life as though she didn't have cancer. "You have to believe you're going to win, experience the joy of each day, and don't give up hope until there really is no hope," she told CNN's Larry King. Remarkable: in the face of Stage 4 metastatic cancer, this drive to make the most of the time that is left. Edwards described her disease as "not curable at this time." There is a certainty about that. And it is uncertainty that can make it difficult for other women to embrace their lives after breast cancer.

"When we talk to women about survival in five-year tranches, we can kill their ability to plan their lives," said Dr. Pignol. He believes some women reclaim that ability when they are told they're cured.

Even if the other C-word doesn't apply, women should be told something. Barb's doctors didn't say very much when she finished treatment. They simply instructed her to come back if she had any symptoms. That's a problem too. "If anything happens, I think it is the big C-word," she said. "If I have a headache, pain, or some shortness of breath I question it."

I asked Dr. Pignol what he would tell a patient such as Barb, who had no evidence of disease after being treated for Stage 3 cancer. "I would say, 'You've had a very good response to chemo, and that's a very good sign. We have done everything we can and given you every chance to avoid a recurrence.'" Sounds good to me. Sounds realistic. Maybe a talk like that would have balanced what Barb heard at the start of her treatment—that she would get a five- to ten-year lease on life.

For my friend Gill, a good deed triggered her anxiety about a relapse. She'd been cancer-free for four years, after Stage 3 lymphoma. But she was getting more and more frightened as the time for her annual CAT scan approached. The problem: Gill had started volunteering in the chemo unit at Toronto's Princess Margaret Hospital—pouring juice, offering cookies and a sympathetic ear. She got to hear all the bad stories, and they got to her. "I should tell them I have to stop doing this when my checkups come around," she said.

My friend Christine also had a lot of anxiety in advance of her semi-annual tests. I talked to her the week before they were scheduled, and she explained that even though she caught her cancer at an early stage, it was unusual. Even the experts weren't sure how to stage it. The tumour was less than one centimetre, but it had already spread. On the other hand, the spread was very limited. Only one lymph node was affected. At Christine's first post-treatment follow-up, the doctors found a spot on her liver. They're pretty sure it's nothing, the equivalent of an age spot, but it has to be followed. "I'm always living with it," said Christine. "It's never over."

Nevertheless, Christine is moving on with her life. She and her boyfriend, Phil, decided to get married in the summer. At first, Christine figured she'd delay setting a date and telling her friends until after she got the results of her big check-up. "I thought, What if I tell people, and it turns out that the cancer is back and I have to do chemo this summer and lose my hair when I was supposed to be getting married?" In the end, she decided against waiting for a green light from the doctors. "You never know," she said, "so you make plans and live life knowing you can get bad news."

As for me, I didn't have a single dark thought before my first follow-ups. Partly, it's the way I'm wired. I put bad things out of my mind as soon as the crisis is past. I did that when my parents went into remission. I responded that way even though I knew their cancers were terminal. The bad news and the gnawing dread were back soon enough.

I feel it's only right to put the cancer behind me. I've finished treatment, and my prognosis is excellent. I feel that my cancer has taken up enough time, energy, and resources. My cancer has had a lot of attention because of my writing. In some ways, that embarrasses me now. The diagnosis was traumatic initially, but I've come to the conclusion that my particular disease was as treatable as it gets. I know I was lucky. It barely slowed me down.

Even though I maintained the fabric of my life throughout my treatment, I took on the identity of Cancergirl. After I accepted myself as a woman living with cancer, I evolved into a woman living well with cancer. But the cancer remained at the centre of everything. It became comfortable—everything I did was judged against it. My co-workers admired me for just showing up at work, my editors praised me for filing stories on time, and my friends would tell me I'm amazing when I turned up to play tennis.

No wonder I bristled when Larissa described my cancer as something that had happened in the past. To let it go meant going back to a place where everything is judged on its own merit, where there is no proviso "for someone who has cancer."

And going back is difficult, because after breast cancer, no one is the same. Not physically and not emotionally. That's what we mean by the "new normal."

The cliché that cancer changes you is true, at least for me. Not only do I look different, but the woman I am now is different from the woman I was then. I'm lucky. I could always handle change. But now I am better able to enjoy life. Since my diagnosis I have felt committed to enjoying life in the moment. My friends say I am a nicer person. I hope it lasts. They say I am "lighter." Maybe that's part of my renewed zest. I know I'll have to be careful not to veer off into a full-on, middle-aged crazy moment.

Dr. Pignol gave me something magical when he told me he considered me cured. It felt like a special gift. But it also felt like something else—a kick in the butt! My radiation oncologist's words were very kind, but I heard something else, a very emphatic: "Get out of my office so I can see some sick people, and move on with your life!" Sometimes you need that kick, in addition to some encouragement. That's what I needed—a push out the door of Cancerland.

I marvel that when it all started—in what's seems like a previous life—I imagined it as Cancerland. For a while, that was an understatement. Cancerworld would have been more like it. But I always thought of it as a place, not a state of being. And since it was a place, I could pick up and leave.

I was ready to leave.

18

Why I Hate the Word
Survivor

The sound of the word makes my hair stand on end. Or it would if I had more hair. When I hear the word survivor, I don't think of myself or the other women I know who have breast cancer. It conjures up an image that is much darker.

WHEN I WAS A KID, my parents used to utter the word in hushed tones. "He's a survivor," my mother would whisper when introducing one of her friends. Today, my parents themselves would be called survivors. They escaped Hitler, waited out the war in the Soviet Union, and immigrated to Canada. But back then, they thought of themselves as displaced persons, refugees, or "green-horns," a Yiddish-English slang word for new immigrants. The word *survivor* was reserved for concentration camp survivors. When my mother said, "He's a survivor," she meant *you'd better behave and be respectful, no matter how strange this person seems.*

And they almost always seemed strange to my childish eyes. I can't think of any reason I should be compared to those sad and broken people I met as a child, or to anyone else who has been through such terror. However, I have to admit the outward similarities are eerie. The postchemo fuzz on my head recalls a survivor's shaved head. Pallor and emaciation can be caused by starvation but can also be a side effect of chemo. Camp inmates had numbers tattooed on their arms, and cancer patients get indelible dot tattoos that ensure the radiation is aimed at the right spot.

It's easy to see the connection. When I was growing up, the word *survivor* was uttered in hushed tones, just like the dreaded C-word. Breast cancer activists have done an admirable job of raising awareness about the disease and bringing it out of the shadows. They've also raised a lot of money, thus enabling many medical breakthroughs that have improved the odds. Maybe throwing the spotlight onto a large group of bald, scarred, one-breasted women helped us get to this point. Given their appearance, perhaps calling them survivors was inspired.

It started with an American physician. In 1985, the *New England Journal of Medicine* published a groundbreaking essay by Dr. Fitzhugh Mullan entitled, "The seasons of survival: reflections of a physician with cancer." Until that point, people with cancer were called victims. There was no concept of living through the disease. Dr. Mullan founded the National Coalition for Cancer Survivorship (NCCS) the following year. That coalition defined survival as living with cancer, as well as living through and beyond cancer. "No matter how long we live, cancer patients are survivors," wrote Dr. Mullan, "at once wary and relieved, bashful and proud." The NCCS took up the business of cancer advocacy, inducing the medical establishment and the government to start dealing with the lifelong impact of cancer, and to create protocols for follow-up. This was a huge advance.

The survivor movement took hold, coinciding with both the rise in patient activism and the women's movement, which challenged paternalism in medicine. By 1996, the U.S. government created the Office of Cancer Survivorship. It does important work. But like many social movements that become institutionalized, the notion of survivorship has become mired in political correctness. What started as a reaction against the concept of cancer patients as victims now smacks of the culture of victimhood.

These days you can earn the title *survivor* by coming through almost any kind of trouble. For that matter, you can be a cancer survivor without ever having cancer. According to the National Cancer Institute, "An individual is considered a cancer survivor from the time of diagnosis through the balance of life. Family members, friends, and caregivers are also impacted by the survivorship experience, and are therefore included in this definition." Expanding the definition of the word *survivor* to include family members and caregivers is fairly recent, but it is universally accepted, at least in North America. I am not making light of other people's pain, but I think this lacks a sense of proportion. If we're *all* survivors, what does the word mean anyway?

When my mother called my attention to a survivor, she was telling me this was someone who had suffered far more than she had, although she lost her entire family. There is a scale of things with cancer too. I had early stage disease and a great prognosis. I can't compare myself to someone whose disease has spread or recurred.

Sometimes I'm almost annoyed when people compliment me on my attitude and tell me "attitude is everything." My disposition is great because my prognosis is. I can't know how I'd react if things were grimmer. A good attitude certainly makes it easier to enjoy the time you have. I applaud Elizabeth Edwards for her dictum, "Live until you die." But I find it hard to believe that she or any other patients with advanced cancer could change their outcomes by being more upbeat.

The survivor label, the platitudes about attitude, and all the talk about cancer as a battle—it's all too politically correct for me. In her 1978 book, *Illness as Metaphor*, Susan Sontag was the first to show how the metaphors surrounding cancer add greatly to the suffering of patients. Cancer, she argued, was not a curse, a punishment, or an embarrassment. I think the metaphors designed to help people *resist* the disease can be just as damaging, and they are now entrenched in our language. I cringe when I read about people who "lose" their "battle" with cancer. It sounds as if it was a personal failing—as if they may not have died if only they'd fought harder.

Sure, it helps to be mentally and physically strong when you're diagnosed. But cancer is a disease, not an epic. Now that the disease is so widespread and commonplace, maybe it's time to put aside the war imagery. I know so many people in the same situation that I don't feel special, singled out, or victimized. That's why I hate being called a survivor. That term was embraced more than twenty years ago. Now we need a new word—a word that conveys the random ordinariness of a cancer diagnosis. Actually, we may need a whole new language—one that will allow us to move past the platitudes about the bravery of simply surviving cancer. Surviving has become the norm, so cancer patients can move beyond survival.

More than ten million Americans and nearly a million Canadians have lived through cancer, and the number of people diagnosed is expected to skyrocket over the next twenty years, as the population ages. If modern life has increased the incidence of cancer, it's because we're living longer. A hundred and fifty years ago, I would likely have died of a childhood disease or in childbirth long before I got breast cancer.

Cancer is one of the bad things that can happen in the ordinary course of living. It's a part of life. Instead of raging and battling and surviving, just living with it may be a better choice. Better still, like the old saying goes—living well is the best revenge.

Index

In the narrative, the names *Abe,* *Allan, Margie, Linda,* and *Larissa* are pseudonyms.

A

Abe (friend), 51
AC/T, 169–170
Adriamycin, 59–60
Allan (friend), 175
Alofs, Paul, 89
Alyn Hospital, 86
anemia, 61–62
Anita (nurse oncologist), 42, 78, 171, 178
Anna (friend), 46–47
Anne (friend), 184
Anne-Marie (friend, radiologist), 25–26, 27, 44, 116
Arimidex, 69
Arnaout, Angel, 11–13, 16–17, 23–25, 26, 28, 30–32, 33, 39, 58, 116, 125, 180
Ashkenazi Jewish population, 26, 116–117, 119
assistants, 10
Ativan, 20, 65

B

bald, 92–93, 95–96
Barb (friend), 104, 184, 193–194, 196
Barbara (friend), 108–109
benign lump, 24

Berger, Bobby, 50, 54
bilateral mastectomies,
123–125, 126, 131–132
biopsy, 12–13, 23–24
bleeding through incision,
33–34
body image, 181–189
Bogyo, Kristine, 166, 168
Bonnie (reader), 79–81,
192–193, 195
Born, Trevor, 40, 125
BRCA-1 gene mutations, 116
BRCA-2 gene mutations, 116,
127, 153, 176
breast cancer
death rate, 165–166
early-stage disease, 45
genetic risk. See genetics
HER2/neu-positive, 167
high risk, and screening,
58–59
invasive ductile carcinoma, 23
multi-focal disease, 46–47
recurrence, 194–195
research, 169–174
sisterhood, 108–109
weight gain, 186
breast reconstruction, 123,
133–134, 135

C
Canadian Association of
Radiologists, 20

Canadian Cancer Society, 4,
165, 172
cancer, spread of, 28–29
Cancer Care Ontario, 9
cancer research, 169–174
Cancer Vixen (Marchetto), 81
Cancergirl, 35–36, 47–48, 198
Cancerland, 36–37, 39, 42, 199
career concerns, 145–151
CAREpath, 8–9, 41–42, 67
Carole (reader), 82
Catherine (reader), 186
cervix, 178–179
Chaya (niece), 163–164
chemotherapy, 4, 31, 57–70,
169–171, 179
children, 54–55, 162–163
choices, 42, 43–48, 120–121
Chrétien, Jean, 148
Christine (friend), 69, 109, 170,
197–198
Classical 96.3 FM, 150
Claudia (Dr. Arnaout's nurse
clinician), 12, 15, 17, 33
CMF, 81
cobalt, 4
colon cancer, 127
cosmetic results, 181–189
cure, 157–162, 167–168,
192–193, 195, 196, 199
Curpen, Belinda, 27–28, 42
cyclophasphamide, 60

D

decision-making, 120–121
delays, effect of, 38
DePetrillo, Denny, 8–9, 41–42
diagnosis, 7–13
Domb, Glicka, 74–76, 82, 87, 88
double bat mitzvah, 164
drug coverage, 64

E

early detection, 19–20, 167
early-stage disease, 45
Edwards, Elizabeth, 147–148, 195–196, 204
Edwards, John, 147–148, 195
Ehrlich, Lisa, 30
Eithne (friend), 104, 108
Elizabeth (reader), 162
Ellie (chemotherapy nurse), 65
Elsa (friend), 71, 73, 74, 104–105, 178
employment issues, 145–151
end of chemotherapy, 67–70
English, Hilde, 52–53, 55, 148–149
English, John, 52, 55, 148–149
Epelzweig, Sarah Tema, 117–118
Esplen, Mary Jane, 77, 181–182, 185, 186–187, 188, 189
exercise, 66, 169, 186

F

Familial Breast Cancer Research Unit (Women's College Hospital), 116
Fern (friend), 105
Flare party, 95–96
friends, 103–113
funding gaps, 9

G

genetic counsellor, 118–119
genetics
    Ashkenazi Jewish population, 26, 116–117, 119
    BRCA-1 gene mutations, 116
    BRCA-2 gene mutations, 116
    continued risks, 131–132
    genetic implications, 115–118
    genetic mutations, 26, 119
    genetic testing, 26–27
    high–risk screening program, 121–123
    making the choice, 134–138
    options, 122–124
    preventive bilateral mastectomies, 123–125, 126, 131–132
    radiation treatment, 132–143
    test results, 126–129
George (boss), 98
Gill (friend), 162, 196–197
Gilmour, David, 51–52, 53–54, 55

Gilmour, Sandra, 51–52, 53–54

Glicka's Wig Design, 74–76

Goold, Doug, 5, 12, 18, 32, 39, 49–56, 74, 85, 95, 96, 98, 145, 169, 181

H

hair loss

bald, 92–93, 95–96

Bonnie's experience, 79–81

buzz cut, 88, 89–90, 91–92

common concerns about, 77–82

the mitzvah wig, 82–83

new hair, 97–101

process of, 87–92

wig vote, 83–86

wigs, 71–76, 81–82, 93–97, 98–99, 108

Haji, Zain, 71–73, 77–78, 89–90, 96

Hamilton, David, 95–96

Helen (Chaya) (mother), 3–4, 53, 78–79, 117–118, 119–120, 163, 201–202

hematoma, 25, 32, 34

Henrietta Banting Breast Centre, 20, 32–33

Herceptin, 167–168

Hereditary and Familial Breast Cancer Unit (Women's College Hospital), 58

high-risk screening program, 121–123

holiday season, 107–109

hormone therapy. *See* tamoxifen

housework, 169

Human Genome Project, 121

husband. *See* Goold, Doug

hysterectomy, 128, 154–155, 175–180

I

ideaCity Conference, 20–21, 145

Illness as Metaphor (Sontag), 204

Imaging Department (Women's College Hospital), 24

inner beauty, 189

intimacy, 187–188

invasive ductile carcinoma, 23

Ivins, Mollie, 81

J

Jeanie (friend), 110–111, 112

Jewish General Hospital (Montreal), 4

Jodi (friend), 93

John (colleague), 97–98, 183

K

King, Mary-Claire, 121

Kingstone, Robert, 2, 7, 8, 19

Kuerti, Anton, 166

L

Laberge, Normand, 20

Larissa (friend), 51, 110, 111–112, 155, 156, 163, 198

leaving Cancerland, 191–200

Leith (nephew), 153, 154, 163–164

Lesley (sister-in-law), 164

life after breast cancer
body image, 181–189
children, concerns of, 162–163
cure or remission, 157–162
doctorless days, 155
end of treatment, 191–193
hysterectomy, 153–155, 175–180
the new normal, 199–200
relapse fears, 194–197
sexuality, 187–188

Life in the Balance (Shapiro), 106–107

Lightstone, Marilyn, 90, 92, 120, 145

Linda (friend), 111, 112, 177–178

Lipa, Joan, 135

the lump, 1–6, 12, 25

lumpectomy, 28, 30–34, 125, 182, 183, 185

lymph nodes, 29–30

lymphedema, 29

M

Madeline (friend), 62, 183

Mak, Tak, 173–174

mammogram, 2–3, 4, 8, 15, 17, 18–20, 25, 38–39, 121, 122

Marchetto, Marisa Acocella, 81

Margie (friend), 136–137

Margolese, Richard, 4

Marvelle Koffler Breast Centre, 8

Mary Lou (friend), 84–85

mastectomy, 4, 5, 16, 26, 182–183, 184. *See also* bilateral mastectomies

McCredie, Eithne, 17–18

McCredie, John, 17–18

McGowan, Anita, 67–68

Mel (friend), 9–10, 11

menopause, 60, 179

Mesley, Wendy, 151

Michina (friend), 90

the mitzvah wig, 82–83

Monika (friend), 106

mother. *See* Helen (Chaya) (mother)

Mount Sinai Hospital, 8

MRI, 20, 25, 122

Mullan, Fitzhugh, 202–203

multi-focal disease, 46–47

multidisciplinary cancer conferences, 24, 25

Murdoch, Sarah, 82, 169

Murphy, Joan, 154, 176, 177, 178–179

N
Narod, Steven, 58, 121–122, 126–128
National Cancer Institute of Canada, 165–166, 203
National Coalition for Cancer Survivorship (NCCS), 203
Neulasta, 64
Neupogen, 64
Nick (friend), 100

O
the odds, 3–4
Office of Cancer Survivorship (U.S.), 203
oncologist, 58–61
options, 15–21
ovarian cancer, 26–27, 116, 120, 127, 128
ovaries, removal of. See hysterectomy

P
parents, 54–55
Pat (friend), 109
pathology report, 30, 33–34
Phillips, David, 38
Pignol, Jean-Philippe, 132, 135–136, 137–138, 139, 142, 157–158, 160, 191–192, 195, 196, 199
plastic surgery. See breast reconstruction
Poll, Aletta, 117, 118–119, 124, 126–127
post-menopausal women, 60
Princess Margaret Hospital, 67, 154
Princess Margaret Hospital Foundation, 89
priorities, 40
prostate cancer, 109, 175
Public Health Agency of Canada, 166

R
radiation, 132–143
radical mastectomy, 4, 5
radiologists' skills, 20
RAPID: Randomized Trial of Accelerated Partial Breast Irradiation, 136–137
recurrence, 194–197
Red Devil, 65
relapse, 194–197
remission, 157–158, 159, 162
Rob (friend), 109
Robyn (reader), 46, 188
Rosh Hashanah, 92
Roy, Steve, 100–101

S

salpingo-oophorectomy, 128,
154–155, 175–180
Scotiabank Giller Prize, 68
secrecy, 149–150
Semple, John, 125, 133–134,
135
sentinel node biopsy, 29–30
seroma, 32
sexuality, 187–188
Shapiro, Marla, 40–41, 50, 54,
106–107, 123, 124, 146
shoe shopping, 91
side effects
Arimidex, 69
chemotherapy, 60, 61, 65–66
lumpectomy, 31–32, 33–34
radiation, 135, 141–142
tamoxifen, 46, 69–70
Slamon, Dennis, 167–168
Smith, Annie, 107–108
socialized medical system,
139
Sontag, Susan, 204
speed, 9
Sperling, Sy and Susan, 84
spouses, 49–56, 181, 187–188
spread of cancer, 28–29
Stacey (MRI nurse), 20
stalactites, 5
Statistics Canada, 166
Stephanie (reader), 46,
187–188, 194–195

Sunnybrook Health Sciences
Centre, 44
Sunnybrook Hospital, 30, 33
Sunnybrook Regional Cancer
Centre (now The Odette
Cancer Centre), 57, 132,
138
support network
friends, 103–113
putting together the treatment
team, 40–41
spousal support, 49–56
surgery
genetic decisions, 123–125,
126
hematoma removal, 34
hysterectomy, 128, 154–155,
175–180
lumpectomy. See lumpectomy
mastectomy. See mastectomy
salpingo-oophorectomy, 128
surgical decisions, 23–34
survival, 165–168
"survivor," 201–205
Susan (Dr. Arnaout's assistant),
10–11
Susan (reader), 85
swelling in breast, 31–32

T

T-cell receptors, 173–174
tamoxifen, 46, 69–70, 121,
122–123, 128, 174

Tanya (nurse oncologist), 135, 137

Taylor, Kathryn, 121

technical artifact, 20

Thelma (ultrasound technician), 27

Thomson, Beverly, 151

Tidal (reader), 85

tissue expanders, 123, 133

tissue transfers, 134

Toronto Sunnybrook Regional Cancer Centre, 8

Toronto Western Hospital, 5

TRAM flap, 134

treatment plan
    chemotherapy, 57–70
    end of treatment, 191–193
    lumpectomy, 28, 30–34
    radiation, 132–143
    surgical decisions, 23–34

treatment team, 9, 41

Turke, Vanessa, 37

U

ultrasounds, 5, 17, 19, 24, 27–28, 122

uterus, 174–175

V

Vicki (friend), 104

W

Wallin, Pamela, 150–151

Warner, Ellen, 44–45, 58–61, 64, 69–70, 74, 86, 121–122, 126, 151, 159–160, 167, 171, 172–173, 179, 182–183, 186, 191–192, 193, 194

weight gain, 185–186

Whylie, Barbara, 172

wig boutique at Princess Margaret Hospital, 71–74, 89–90

wig vote, 83–86

wigs, 71–76, 81–82, 93–97, 98–99, 108

Wolfe, Gordy, 166

Women's College Hospital, 10–11, 17, 20, 24, 33, 125

work, 145–151

writing, 149–150

Y

Yona (wig owner), 83

Z

Znaimer, Moses, 20–21, 62, 90, 99, 145

Znaimer, Sam, 145